150 of the best JAZZ STANDARDS ever!

GW00770993

Exclusive Distributors:
Music Sales Limited
14-15 Berners Street, London W1T 3LJ, UK.

Order No. HLE90003199
ISBN 1-84609-607-3

Cover design by Chloë Alexander
Printed in Great Britain

Your Guarantee of Quality
As publishers, we strive to produce every book to the highest commercial standards.
The book has been carefully designed to minimise awkward page turns and to make playing from it a real pleasure.
Throughout, the printing and binding have been planned to ensure a sturdy, attractive publication which should give years of enjoyment.
If your copy fails to meet our high standards, please inform us and we will gladly replace it.

www.musicsales.com

HLE
Hal Leonard Europe
Distributed by Music Sales

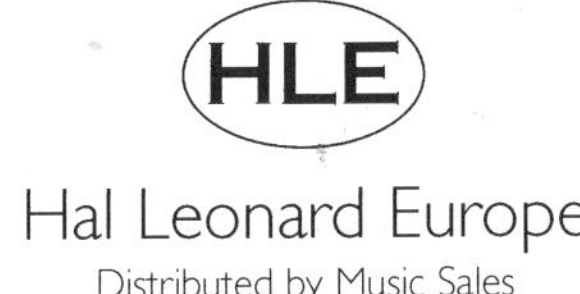

AIN'T MISBEHAVIN'

from AIN'T MISBEHAVIN'

Words by ANDY RAZAF
Music by THOMAS "FATS" WALLER
and HARRY BROOKS

E♭ G7 C7
3fr
Here is one bird with self - con - trol;
That's why my con - science nev - er sleeps;
F9 B♭13 B♭7♯5 E♭ B♭7♯5 E♭ B7
6fr 6fr 3fr 6fr 3fr
Hap - py in - side my cage.
When you're a - way some - where.
I know who I love
Sure was a luck - y
E E♭ B7 E
3fr
best,
day,
Thumbs down for all the rest,
When fate sent you my way,
E♭ Cm7 Cm6 E♭m6 G/D A7 D13
3fr 3fr 3fr 4fr
My love was giv - en, heart and soul;
And made you mine a - lone for keeps,
So it can stand the
Dit - to to all you

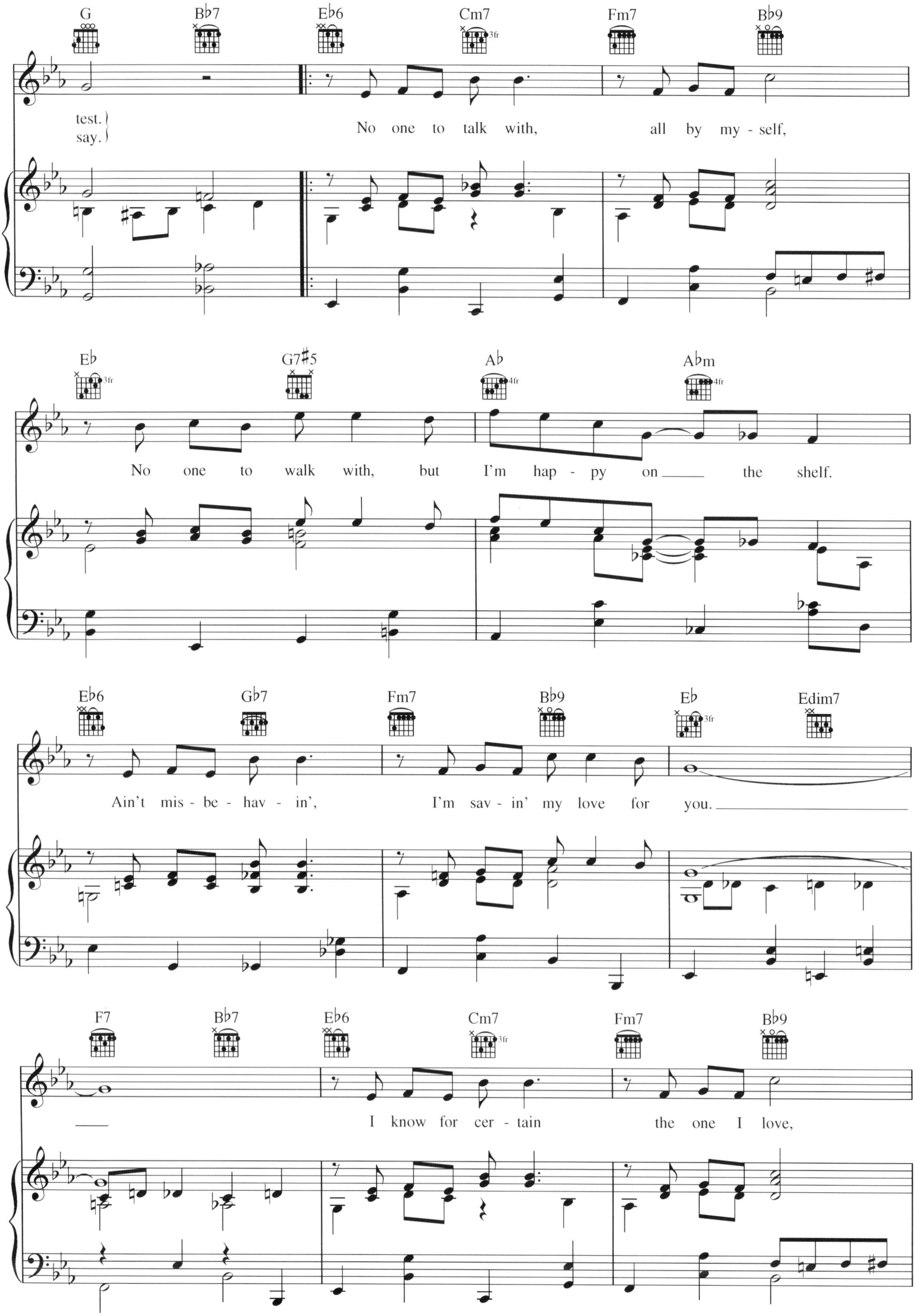
G
B♭7
E♭6
Cm7
3fr
Fm7
B♭9
test.
say.
No one to talk with, all by my - self,
E♭
3fr
G7♯5
A♭
4fr
A♭m
4fr
No one to walk with, but I'm hap - py on the shelf.
E♭6
G♭7
Fm7
B♭9
E♭
3fr
Edim7
Ain't mis - be - hav - in', I'm sav - in' my love for you.
F7
B♭7
E♭6
Cm7
3fr
Fm7
B♭9
I know for cer - tain the one I love,

Eb G7#5 Ab Abm Eb6 Gb7

I'm through with flirt - in', it's just you I'm think - in' of. Ain't mis - be - hav - in',

Fm7 Bb9 Eb Abmaj7 Eb7 G7

I'm sav - in' my love for you.

Cm Ab7/C F7/C

Like Jack Hor - ner in the cor - ner, don't go no - where,

C7 Bb Cm7 F7

what do I care, Your kiss - es are worth wait - in'

B♭7 C7 F9 B♭7 E♭6 Cm7
for, be - lieve me. I don't stay out late,
Fm7 B♭9 E♭ G7♯5 A♭ A♭m
don't care to go, I'm home a - bout eight, just me and my ra - di - o.
E♭ G♭7 Fm7 B♭9
Ain't mis - be - hav - in', I'm sav - in' my love for
1
E♭ C13
you.
F13 B♭13
2
E♭ B♭9 E♭
you.

ALL OR NOTHING AT ALL

Words by JACK LAWRENCE
Music by ARTHUR ALTMAN

Gm7(add13)
3fr
A♭dim7♯13
Am7
lose con - trol of my heart and soul when I'm near you.
Gm/B♭
G6/B
Am6/C
C♯m7
4fr
Em7
Gdim7
That's why I fear you and turn a -
D6
B+
Em9
way. I need a love that's true.
F9
F♯dim7
Dm7(add13)
5fr
Cmaj7/G
I wish it could be you, I know it

Fm6/A♭
6fr
Am11
3fr
G♯dim7
G11
should be you and so I
F13♯11
B♭9
Slowly, with much expression
Am
Am(maj7)
say: All or noth - ing at
3
p
Am7
Am6
Am♭13
Am
Am6
Am(maj7)
Am7
all! Half a love nev - er ap -
B♭9
Gm/B♭
B♭maj7♯5
6fr
B♭7
Gm
3fr
Gm6
3fr
pealed to me. If your heart nev - er could

Dm
G7
G7♯5
yield to me, then I'd rath - er have noth - ing at
Cmaj9
C6
Bm7
E7
Am
Am(maj7)
all! All or noth - ing at
Am7
Am6
Am♭13
Am
Am6
Am(maj7)
Am7
all! If it's love, there is no
B♭9
Gm/B♭
B♭maj7♯5
B♭7
Gm
Gm6
in be - tween. Why be - gin, then cry for some - thing that

Dm
G7
G7♯5
might have been.
No, I'd rath - er have noth - ing at
Cmaj9
C6
B♭m7
E♭7
A♭
A♭+
all.
But, please, don't bring your
A♭6
A♭+
A♭
A♭maj7♯5
A♭6
A♭maj7♯5
E♭
3fr
4fr
lips so close to my cheek.
Don't
A♭
A♭maj7♯5
D♭/A♭
A♭
E♭9
Cm/E♭
smile, or I'll be lost be - yond re - call.

E♭maj7♯5
E♭7
B♭m7/A♭
E♭7
B♭m7/F
E♭7/G
The kiss in your eyes, the touch of your hand makes me
B♭m7
E♭7
Gm7♭5
C7
Fm
weak, and my heart may grow
D♭9
C7
E7♭9
diz - zy and fall. And if I
Am
Am(maj7)
Am7
fell un - der the spell of your call,

Am6
Am♭6
Am
Am6
Am(maj7)
Am7
B♭9
Gm/B♭
I would be caught in the un - der - tow.
B♭maj7♯5
B♭7
Gm
Gm6
So, you see, I've got to say:
Dm
E7♭9
Am
Fm6
No! No! All or noth - ing at
C
E7♭9
all!
C
C6
all!

AIN'T THAT A KICK IN THE HEAD

Words by SAMMY CAHN
Music by JAMES VAN HEUSEN

B♭7
B♭7sus
B♭7
Fm7
Fm7/B♭
The room was com - plete - ly black;
Fm7
B♭9
Fm7
Fm7/B♭
Fm7
B♭9
I hugged her and she hugged back! Like the
B♭7♯5
6fr
E♭maj9
sail - or said, quote, "Ain't that a hole in the boat?"
E♭6
E♭maj9
E♭6
G7
My head keeps spin - ning, I go to sleep and keep

Cm
F7
grin - ning! If this is just the be - gin - ning,
Fm7
Bb7#5(b9)
my life is gon - na be bee - u - tee - ful!
I've sun -
She's tell -
Eb
Db7b5
C7
- shine e - nough to spread; it's just like the fel - la said.
- ing me we'll be wed, she's picked out a king - sized bed;
1.
C7/Bb
Am7b5
Bb9sus
Tell me quick, ain't love a kick in the head?

E♭6
2.
F♯7
How luck - I could -
F7
B♭9
Fm6/A♭
6fr
- n't feel an - y bet - ter or I'd be sick!
Gm7♭5
C7
C7/B♭
5fr
Am7♭5
Tell me quick, ain't love a
B♭9sus
E♭6
E♭maj9
kick in the head?

ALFIE

Theme from the Paramount Picture ALFIE

Words by HAL DAVID
Music by BURT BACHARACH

Very slowly, rubato

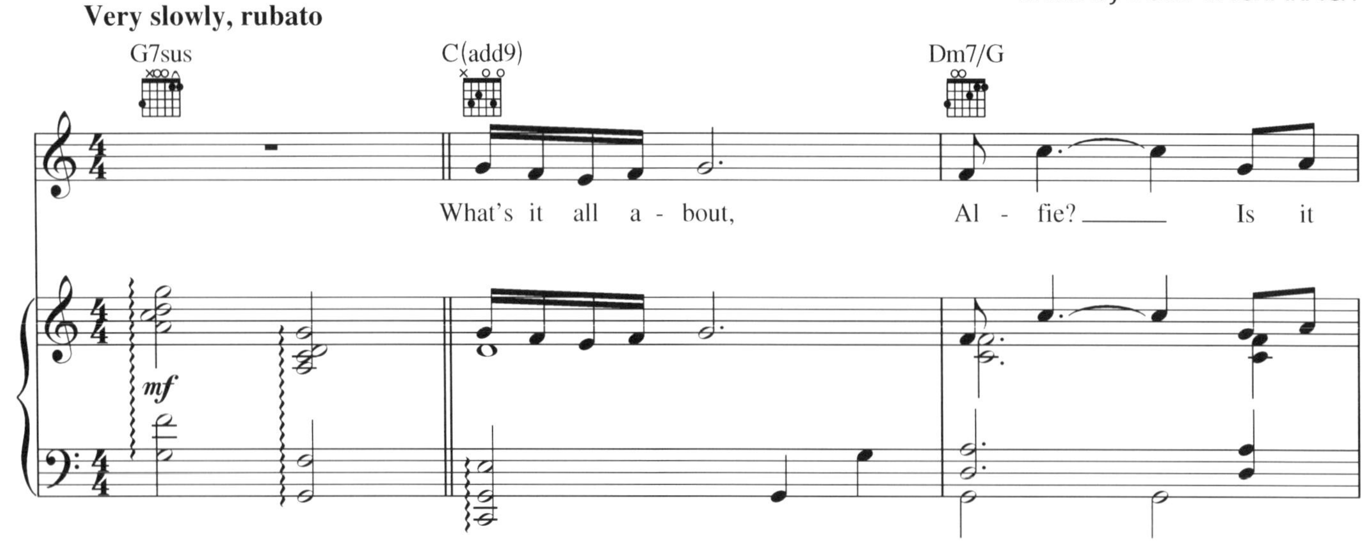

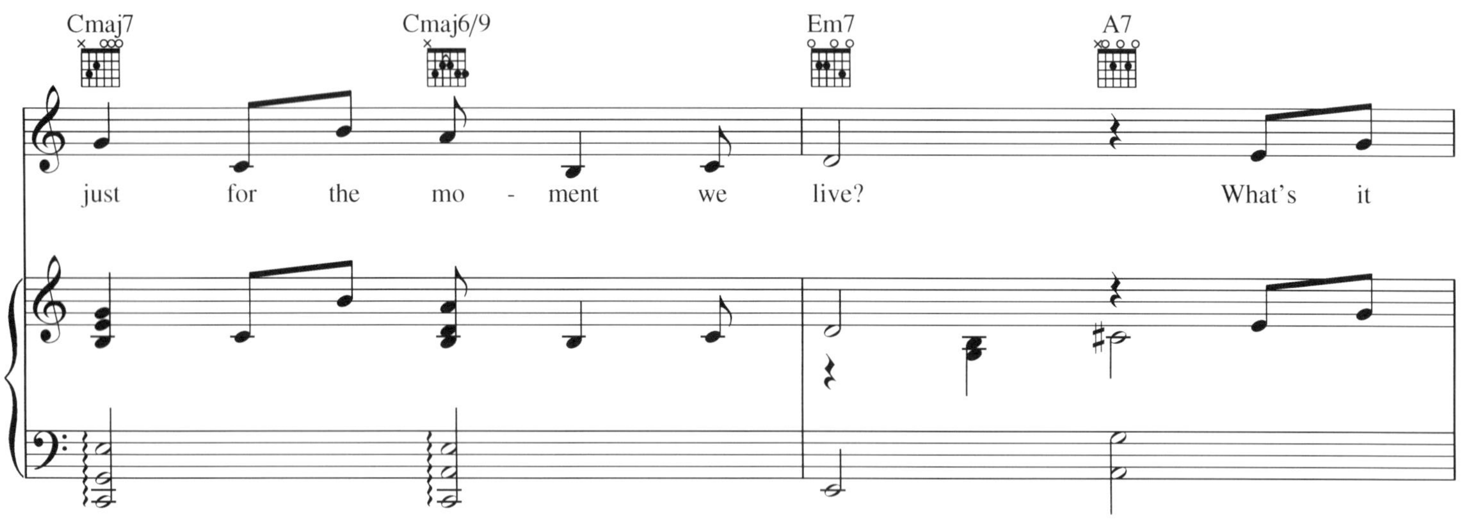

Dm7
Dm7/G
Cdim7
Dm7/G
Are we meant to take more than we give, or are we meant to be kind?
G13
G9♯5
3fr
3fr
C(add9)
Dm7/G
And if on - ly fools are kind, Al - fie, then I
Cmaj7
Cmaj6/9
Em7
A7
Dm7
guess it is wise to be cruel. And if life be - longs on - ly to the strong,
Em7
Am7
Dm7
Dm7/G
Cdim7
Al - fie, what will you lend on an old gold - en rule? As

Bm7
E♭6/D
Am7/D
sure as I be - lieve there's a heav - en a -
Bm7
Am7/D
Bm7
bove, Al - fie, I know there's some - thing much
E♭6/D
Am7/D
Dm7/G
G9
G13
G9
more, some - thing e - ven non - be - liev - ers can be - lieve in.
C(add9)
Dm7/G
F♯m7♭5
F9
I be - lieve in love, Al - fie. With - out true love we just ex -

Em7
Am7
F♯m7♭5
F9
ist, Al - fie. Un - til you find the love you've
Em7
Am7
D9♯11
Dm7/G
missed you're noth - ing, Al - fie. When you walk let your heart
rall.
L.H.
a tempo
F♯dim7
Dm7/G
lead the way, and you'll find love an - y day, Al - fie,
rall.
dim. poco a poco
Dm9
C7♭9
Cmaj9
Cmaj7
Al - fie.
pp

ALL OF ME

Words and Music by SEYMOUR SIMONS
and GERALD MARKS

Am D7 G7 D7/F♯ G7♭9/F

one - sid - ed love ___ af - fair? All you took, I

C/E Cdim7/E♭ Dm A7/C♯ A♭7/C G7 G7♯5

glad - ly gave, there's noth - ing left for me to save.

C E7

All of me, ___ why not take all of me? ___

A7

___ Can't you see ___ I'm no good with -

Dm
E7
out you?
Take my lips,
I want to
Am
D7
lose them.
Take my arms,
G7
I'll nev - er use
them.
C
E7
Your good - bye
left me with
eyes that cry,

A7
how can I go on, dear, with-
3
Dm
F6
Fm6
out you?
You took the part that
C/E
Gm/B♭
A7
Dm7♭5
G7
once was my heart,
so why not take all of
1
C
E♭dim7
Dm7
G7♯5
2
C
Fm
C
me?
me?
8va

ALL THE THINGS YOU ARE

from VERY WARM FOR MAY

Lyrics by OSCAR HAMMERSTEIN II
Music by JEROME KERN

B7sus
B7
G
touch - ing your hand, my heart beats the fast - er. All that I want in
D7sus
D7
G
C7
B♭/C
C7
all of this world is you.
Fm7
B♭m7
E♭9
E♭7♭9
A♭maj7
You are the prom - ised kiss of spring - time that
D♭maj7
G7
G7♭5
Cmaj7
Bmaj7
Cmaj7
Cmaj9
C6
makes the lone - ly win - ter seem long.

Cm7
3fr
Fm7
B♭9
E7
E♭maj7
3fr
You are the breath - less hush of eve - ning that
A♭maj9
3fr
Am7♭5
D7
Gmaj9
Gm6/B♭
trem - bles on the brink of a love - ly song.
You are the
Am7
D9
4fr
Gmaj7
G6
Am7
Gmaj7
an - gel glow that lights a star,
the dear - est
F♯m7♭5
4fr
B7♭9
Emaj9
E6
C7♭9
C7
things I know are what you are.

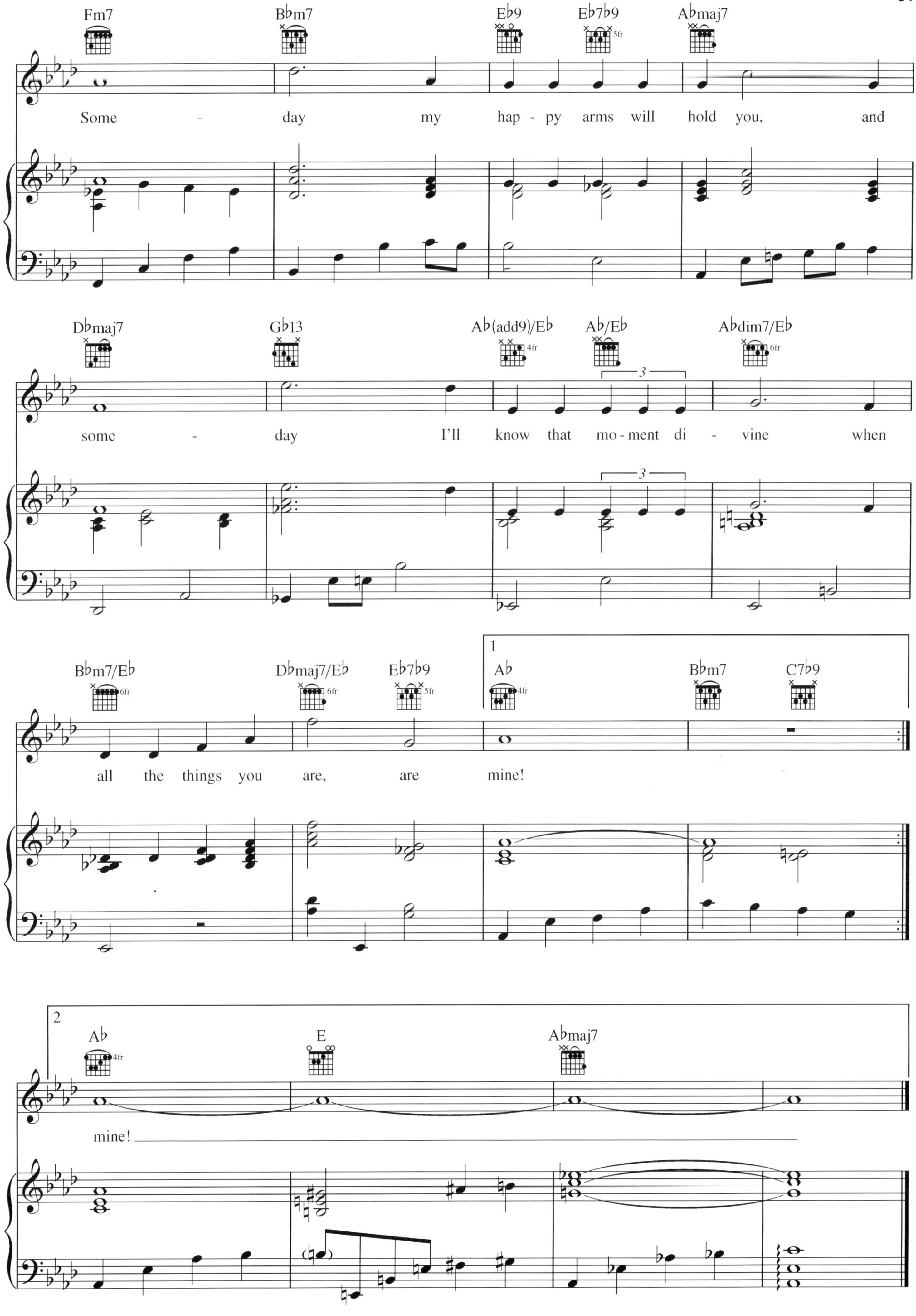
Fm7 B♭m7 E♭9 E♭7♭9 A♭maj7
5fr
Some - day my hap - py arms will hold you, and
D♭maj7 G♭13 A♭(add9)/E♭ A♭/E♭ A♭dim7/E♭
4fr 6fr
some - day I'll know that mo - ment di - vine when
3
B♭m7/E♭ D♭maj7/E♭ E♭7♭9 A♭ B♭m7 C7♭9
6fr 6fr 5fr 4fr
1
all the things you are, are mine!
2
A♭ E A♭maj7
4fr
mine!

ALL THE WAY

Words by SAMMY CAHN
Music by JAMES VAN HEUSEN

G7
1
Cm
B♭m7
E♭7♭5
A♭
that's how it's got to feel.
on - ly a fool would
Deep - er than the
B♭7
Bdim
Cm
F7
Fm7♭5
B♭7
deep blue sea is, that's how deep it goes, if it's real.
2
Cm
A♭m6
C♭
E♭
D♭9
C7
Am7♭5
Fm6/A♭
say. But if you let me love you, it's for sure I'm gon - na love you all the
Gm7♭5
C7
Fm7♭5
B♭7♭5
E♭
D♭9
E♭6/9
way, all the way.

ALRIGHT, OKAY, YOU WIN

Words and Music by SID WYCHE
and MAYME WATTS

A♭
o - kay, you win,
E♭ E♭ B♭7 B7 C7♯5 D♭7♯5
ba - by, what can I do? I'll do an - y - thing you say,
A♭9 E♭ A♭7 E♭
it's just got - ta be that way. Well, al - right,
B♭+ E♭ B♭+ E♭
o - kay, you win, I'm in
4fr
3fr
8fr

E♭7
A♭
4fr
love with you. Well, al - right, o - kay, you win,
E♭
3fr
B♭7
B7
C7♯5
8fr
D♭7♯5
3fr
Ba - by, what can I do? An - y-thing you say I'll do,
A♭9
4fr
E♭
3fr
A♭7
4fr
E♭
3fr
as long as it's me and you.
E♭6
A♭7
4fr
E♭6
A♭7
4fr
All that I am ask - in', all I want from you,

E♭6
A♭9
4fr
just love me like I love you an' it
E♭
3fr
N.C.
B♭7
N.C.
E♭
3fr
B♭7
won't be hard to do! Well, al - right, o - kay,
E♭
3fr
B♭+
E♭
3fr
E♭7
you win, I'm in love with you! Well, al - right,
A♭
4fr
E♭
3fr
o - kay, you win,
ba - by,
ba - by,

Bb7
B7
C7#5
Db7#5
1
Ab9
what can I do?
I'll do an-y-thing you say.
It's
one thing more,
if you're gon-na be my man,
Eb
Ab7
Eb
2
Ab9
just got to be that way.
Well, al-right,
sweet ba-
Eb
Ab6
Ab9
Eb
Ab
Eb/G
Eb
-by, take me by the hand.
Well, al-right,
o-kay,
Ab
Eb/G
Ab
Eb/G
Eb7/G
Ab
Fm7b5
Bb7
Bb7#5
Eb9
you win.

ANGEL EYES

Words by EARL BRENT
Music by MATT DENNIS

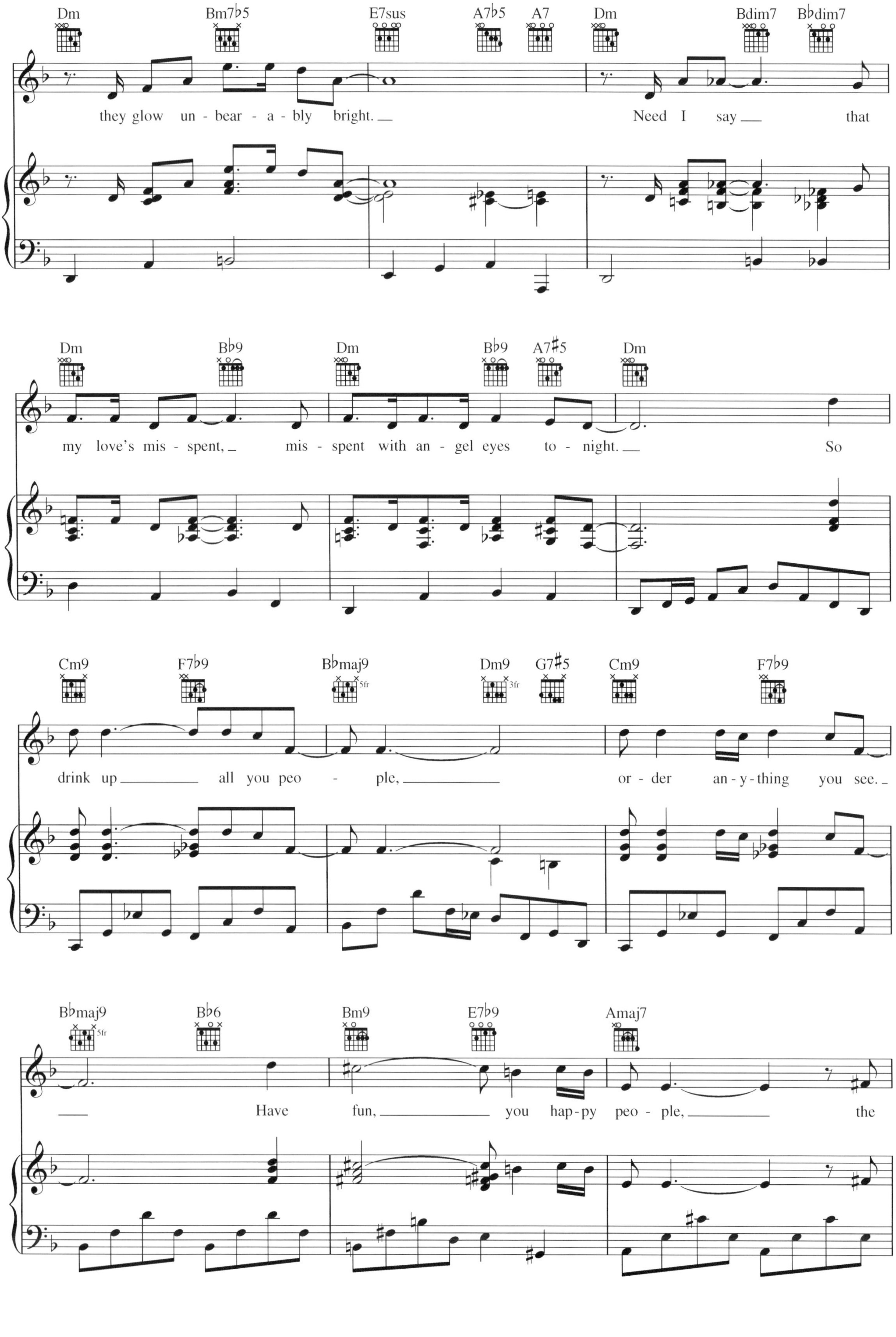
Dm Bm7♭5 E7sus A7♭5 A7 Dm Bdim7 B♭dim7
they glow un - bear - a - bly bright. Need I say that
Dm B♭9 Dm B♭9 A7♯5 Dm
my love's mis - spent, mis - spent with an - gel eyes to - night. So
Cm9 F7♭9 B♭maj9 Dm9 G7♯5 Cm9 F7♭9
drink up all you peo - ple, or - der an - y - thing you see.
B♭maj9 B♭6 Bm9 E7♭9 Amaj7
Have fun, you hap - py peo - ple, the
5fr
3fr
5fr

D♯m
G♯13
E7sus
A7♯5
Dm
Bdim7
B♭dim7
Dm
B♭9
A7♭9
drink and the laughs on me.
Par-don me, but I got-ta run,
Dm
Bm7♭5
E7sus
A7♭5
A7
Dm
Bdim7
B♭dim7
the fact's un-com-mon-ly clear.
Got-ta find who's
Dm
B♭9
Dm
B♭9
A7♯5
1
Dm
Em7♭5
A7♯5
now "Num-ber One" and why my An-gel Eyes ain't here.
2 Dm
B♭9
A7♯5(♯9)
Dm6/9
Dm(maj9)
'Scuse me while I dis-ap-pear.

BETWEEN THE DEVIL AND THE DEEP BLUE SEA

from RHYTHMANIA

Lyric by TED KOEHLER
Music by HAROLD ARLEN

Gm7 3fr C7 F D♭7 4fr C7
I sup - pose you'll tell me I'm all wrong. It's a
F F7 Dm B♭m
bit - ter pill to take, com - ing from you, tho' I've made a big mis - take,
Gm7 3fr C7 F Gm7 3fr C7 F
what can I do? I don't know what makes me string a - long.
C7♯5 8fr F Gm7 3fr C7 F
I don't want you, but I'd hate to

Gm7 C7 F7 B♭ B♭m6 F/C Fm6 Gm7 C7
3 fr
6 fr
3 fr
lose you. You've got me in be - tween _ the de - vil and the deep blue sea. _
F C7 F Gm7 C7 F
3 fr
_ I for - give you, 'cause I can't for -
Gm7 C7 F7 B♭ B♭m6 F/C Fm6/C Gm7 C7
3 fr
6 fr
6 fr
3 fr
get you. You've got me in be - tween _ the de - vil and the deep blue sea. _
F E7 A6 Bm7 E7
2 fr
_ I ought to cross you off my list, _

A Adim A F7♯5 E7 Am6 C/G
5 fr
but when you come knock - ing at my door. _ Fate seems to give my
Fm6 A♭7 Dm7♭5 G7 C7 F
4 fr
heart a twist, _ and I come run - ning back for more. I should
Gm7 C7 F Gm7 C7 F7
3 fr
hate you, but I guess I love you. You've got me
B♭ B♭m6 F/C Fm6/C Gm7 C7
6 fr
1 F Cdim7 C7
2 F
in be - tween _ the de - vil and the deep blue sea. _ _

BEWITCHED
from PAL JOEY

Words by LORENZ HART
Music by RICHARD RODGERS

Dm7
G7
Cmaj7
C6
Dm7
G7
Since this half - pint im - i - ta - tion, Put me on the blink. I'm
rit.
Slowly
C
G7/D
C/E
C+/E
wild a - gain, be - guiled a - gain, a sim - per - ing, whim - per - ing
p a tempo
F
Ddim7
C/E
D7
G7
A7
child a - gain, Be - witched, both - ered and be - wil - dered am
Dm
G7
C
G7/D
I. Could - n't sleep, and would - n't sleep, When
mf
p

C/E C+/E F Ddim7 C/E D7
love came and told me I shouldn't sleep, Be - witched, both - ered and be -
G7 C7 F A7
wil - dered am I.
Dm Dm7 Am
Lost my heart, but what of it? He is cold, I a -
mp
Dm7 G7 Dm7/G G7
gree, He can laugh, but I love it, Al - though the

Em7 E♭dim7 Dm7 G7 C

laugh's on me. I'll sing to him, each

mf *p*

G7/D C/E C+/E F Ddim7

spring to him, And long for the day when I'll cling to him, Be -

C/E D7 G9 1 C Am

witched, both - ered and be - wil - dered am I.

Dm7 G7 2 C F C6

I'm I. ____________________

sf

BEYOND THE SEA

Words and Music by CHARLES TRENET,
ALBERT LASRY and JACK LAWRENCE

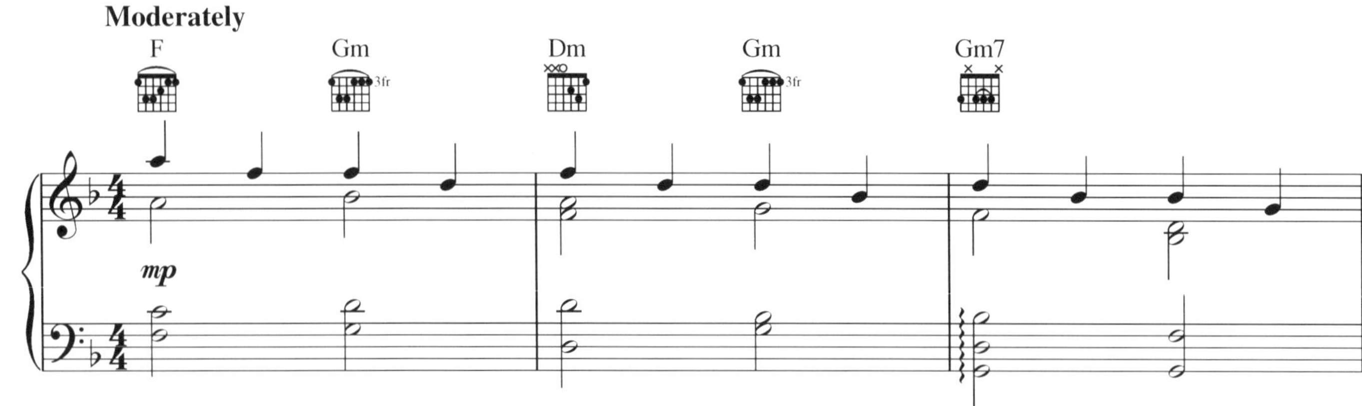

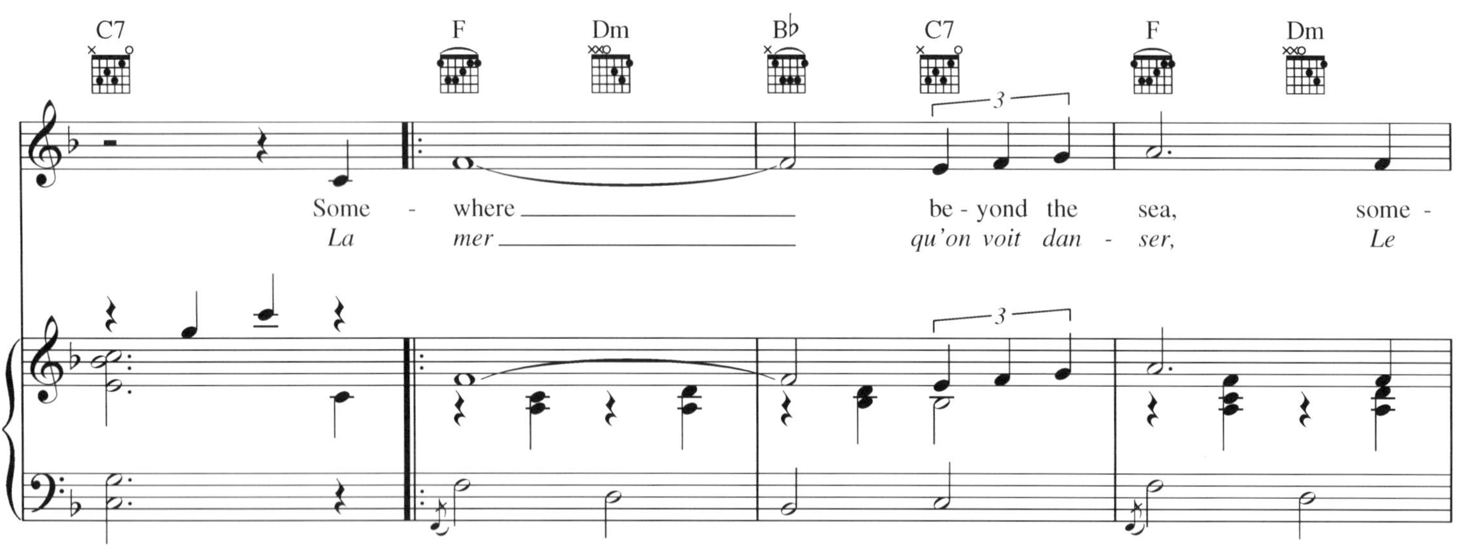

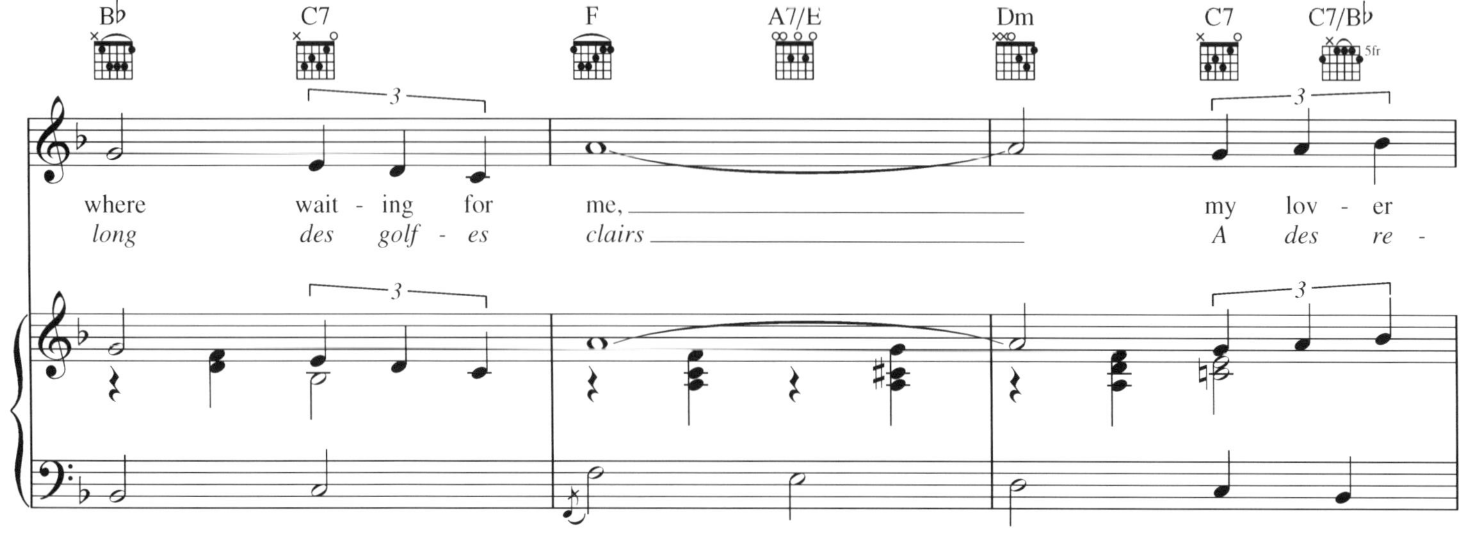

F/A Dm B♭ D7/A Gm C7 C♯dim
3fr
4fr
stands on gold - en sands and watch - es the
flets d'ar - gent la mer, Des re - flets change -
Dm B♭ G7 C C7/B♭ F Dm
5fr
ships that go sail - ing. Some - where
ants sous la plu - ie. La mer
B♭ C7 F Dm B♭ C7
be - yond the sea, he's she's there watch - ing for
au ciel d'é - té Con - fond ses blancs mou -
F A7/E Dm C7 C7/B♭ F/A Dm B♭ D7/A
5fr
me. If I could fly like birds on high,
tons A - vec les anges si purs, la mer

Gm
C7
C♯dim
Dm
B♭
Gm7
C7
F
E7
then straight to his/her arms I'd go sail - ing. It's
Ber - gér - e d'a - zur in - fi - ni - e Voy -
A
F♯m7
D6
E7
A
F♯m7
far be - yond a star; it's
ez près des é - tangs Ces
D6
E7
A
A/G♯
A/F♯
A/E
G7
C
Am
near be - yond the moon. I know
grands ro - seaux mouil - llés. Voy - ez
F
G7
C
Am
F6
G7
be - yond a doubt, my heart will lead me there
ces oi - seaux blancs Et ces mai - sons roui -

C C/B♭ Am C7 F Dm B♭ C7
soon. We'll meet be - yond the
llées. La mer les a ber -
F Dm B♭ C7 F A7/E Dm C7 C7/B♭
shore; we'll kiss just as be - fore. Hap - py we'll
cés Le long des golf - es clairs Et d'une chan -
F/A Dm B♭ D7/A Gm C7 C♯dim Dm B♭
be be - yond the sea, and nev - er a - gain I'll go
son d'a mour, la mer A ber - cé mon coeur pour la
1 G7 C7 F Gm7 C7 2 G7 C7 F
sail - ing. Some - sail - ing.
vi - e. La vi - e.

BLUE IN GREEN

By MILES DAVIS

Slowly

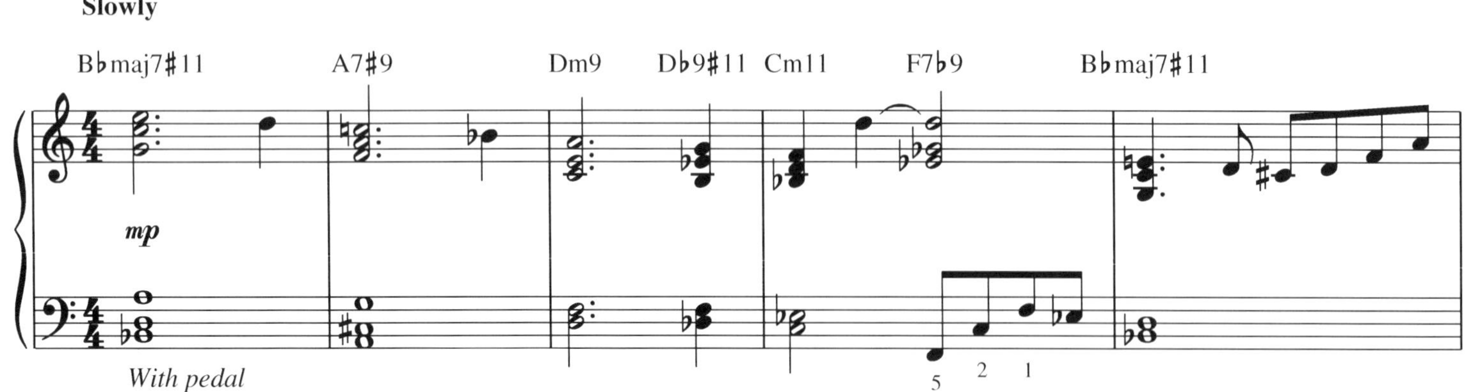

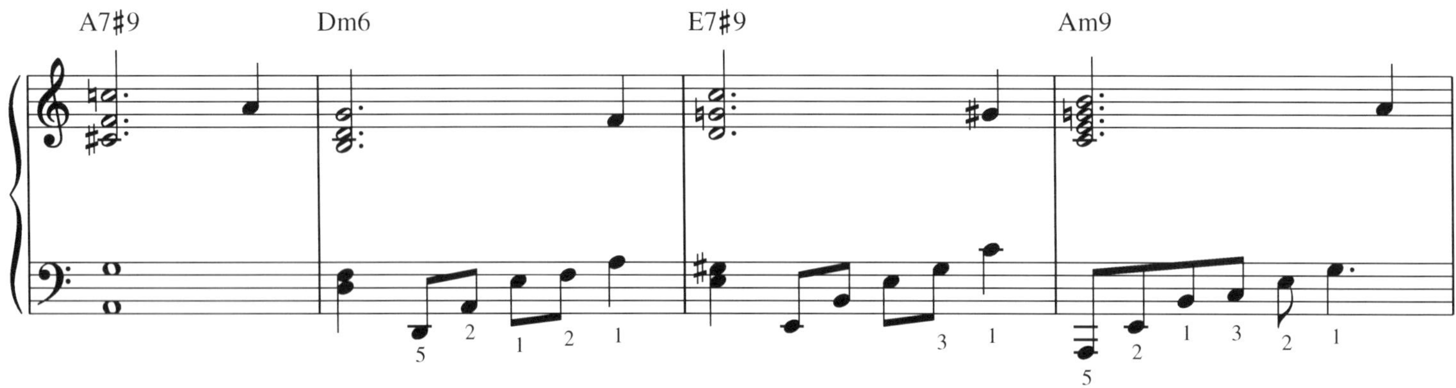

A7#9
Dm6
E7#9
Am(maj7)
Am7
Dm9
B♭maj7#11
A7#9
Dm9
D♭7#11
Cm11
F7♭9
B♭maj7#11
A7#9
Dm6/9
E7#9
Am9
Dm7
B♭maj7#11
A7#9
Dm9

THE BLUE ROOM
from THE GIRL FRIEND

Words by LORENZ HART
Music by RICHARD RODGERS

B♭
F
D7
Gm
3fr
D7
Gm
3fr
D7
Here's the kid - dies' room, Here's the bid - dy's room, Here's a pan - try
8va
Gm7
C7
F6
C7
Fmaj7
B♭
Fmaj7
lined with shelves, dear. Here I've planned for us, Some - thing
B♭
Fmaj7
B♭
B♭maj7/A
5fr
Gm7
C7
grand for us, Where we two can be our - selves, dear.
Slowly, with expression
F
C7
F
We'll have a blue room, a new room, For

C7 F Fmaj7 F7 B♭ Gm7 F G7
two room, Where ev - 'ry day's a hol - i - day Be - cause you're mar - ried to
C7 F C7 F
me. Not like a ball - room, A small room, A
C7 F Fmaj7 F7 B♭ Gm7 F Gm7 C7
hall room, Where {I you} can smoke {my your} pipe a - way, With {your my} wee head up - on {my your}
F C7 F
knee. We will thrive on, keep a - live on Just noth - ing but

C7 Gm7 C7 Dm7 G7
kiss - es, With Mis - ter and Mis - sus On lit - tle blue
C7 F C7 F
chairs. You sew your / I'll wear my trous - seau, And Rob - in - son
C7 F Fmaj7 F7 B♭ Gm7
Cru - soe Is not so far from world - ly cares As our
F Gm7 C7 1 F Gm7 C7 2 F
blue room far a - way up - stairs! stairs!
poco rall.
rit.

BLUESETTE

Words by NORMAN GIMBEL
Music by JEAN THIELEMANS

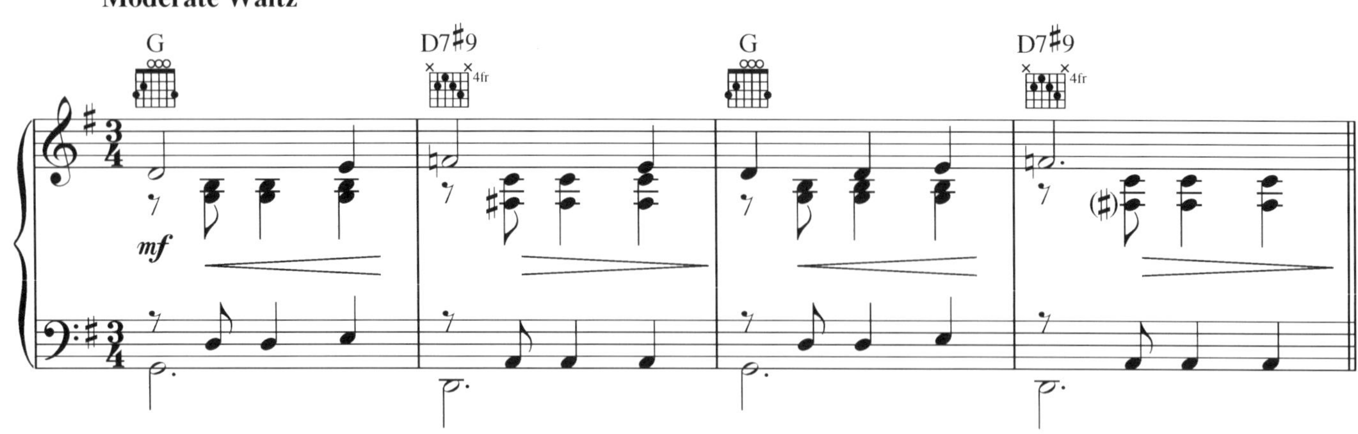

Cmaj7
C6
Cm7
3fr
F9
You can bet one luck - y day, you'll wak - en
Some blue boy is long - ing, just like you, to
Bbmaj7
Bb6
Bbm7
Eb9
and your blues will be for - sak - en.
find a some - one to be true to.
Ab
4fr
Am7b5
D9
4fr
One luck - y day, love - ly love will come your
Two lov - ing arms he can nes - tle in and
Bm7
Bb7
Am7
D7
way.
stay.

G
F♯m7♭5
4fr
B7
Get set, Blues - ette,
true love is com - ing.
Em7
A7
Dm7
G7
Your trou - bled heart
soon will be hum - ming.
Cmaj7
C6
Cm7
3fr
F7
Hum
B♭maj7
B♭6
B♭m7
E♭9

A♭
Am7♭5
D9
4fr
Doo - ya, Doo - ya, Doo - ya,
Doo - ya, Doo - ya, Doo - ya,
Doo - oo - oo
Blues -
Bm7
B♭7
Am7
D7
ette.
G
F♯m7♭5
B7
Pret - ty lit - tle Blues - ette
must - n't be a mourn - er.
Em7
A7
Dm7
G7
Have you heard the news yet?
Love is 'round the cor - ner.

Cmaj7
C6
Cm7
3fr
F7
Love wrapped in rain - bows and tied with pink rib - bon to
B♭maj7
B♭6
B♭m7
E♭7
make your next Spring - time your gold wed - ding ring time. So,
A♭
4fr
Am7♭5
D7
dry your eyes. Don't - cha pout, don't - cha fret, good - y
Bm7
B♭7
Am7
D7
good times are com - ing, Blues - ette.

G
F♯m7♭5
4fr
B7♭9
Long as there's love in your heart to share,
Em7
A7♭9
5fr
Dm7
G7
dear Blues - ette, don't de - spair.
Cmaj7
C6
Cm7
3fr
F9
Some blue boy is long - ing, just like you, to
B♭maj7
B♭6
B♭m7
E♭9
find a some - one to be true to.

A♭
4fr
Am7♭5
D9
4fr
One luck - y day, love - ly love will come your
Bm7
E7
E7♯5
E7
way. That mag - ic
Am7
D7
day may just be to -
G
D7♯9
4fr
D9
4fr
Bm7
Am7
A♭maj7
Gmaj7
day.
molto rit.

BYE BYE BLACKBIRD

Lyric by MORT DIXON
Music by RAY HENDERSON

Gm7/C
Gm7♭5
C7
F
F+
F6
F
- shine ga - lore.
will come true.
Pack up all my care and woe,
Gm7
C9
F6
F/A
A♭dim7
Gm7
C7
Here I go sing - ing low, Bye bye black - bird.
Gm
Gm♯5
Gm6
Gm
C9
Where some - bod - y waits for me, Sug - ar's sweet,
Gm7
C9
Gm7
C7
Fmaj7
F6
so is she, Bye bye black - bird.

F7 Am7♭5 D7 Gm Gm7♭5
No one here can love and un - der - stand me. Oh, what hard luck
F G7 B♭m6/D♭ C7 F F+
sto - ries they all hand me; Make my bed and
F6 F Gm7 C9 Am7♭5 D7 Gm
light the light, I'll ar - rive late to - night, black - bird
C7 1 F Dm Gm7 C7 2 F Gm7/D Gm7♭5 F6
bye bye. bye.

CALL ME IRRESPONSIBLE

from the Paramount Picture PAPA'S DELICATE CONDITION

Words by SAMMY CAHN
Music by JAMES VAN HEUSEN

Dm7/G G7 Gm7/C Gm7 C7
Well, I'm not too clev - er. I just a - dore you.
R.H.
F F6 F♯dim7 Gm Gm6
Call me un - pre - dict - a - ble, tell me
G♯dim7 Fmaj7/A F A7
I'm im - prac - ti - cal, rain - bows I'm in - clined to pur -
D7 Gm
sue.
Call me
mf

Cdim7
C7
Am7♭5
D9
4fr
ir - re - spon - si - ble, yes, I'm un - re - li - a - ble,
Gm
3fr
Cdim7
C7
A7
but it's un - de - ni - a - bly true,
D7♭9
4fr
D7
Gm
3fr
C7♭9
3
I'm ir - re - spon - si - bly mad for
1
F
Gm7/C
Fmaj7
Gm7/C
2
F
Fmaj7
you!
you!
p

CAN'T HELP LOVIN' DAT MAN

from SHOW BOAT

Lyrics by OSCAR HAMMERSTEIN II
Music by JEROME KERN

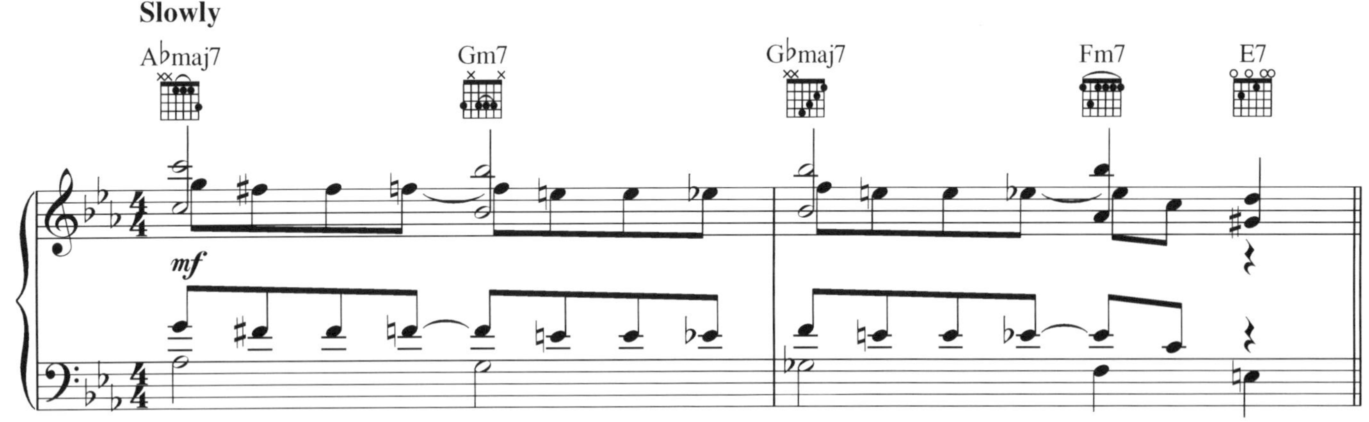

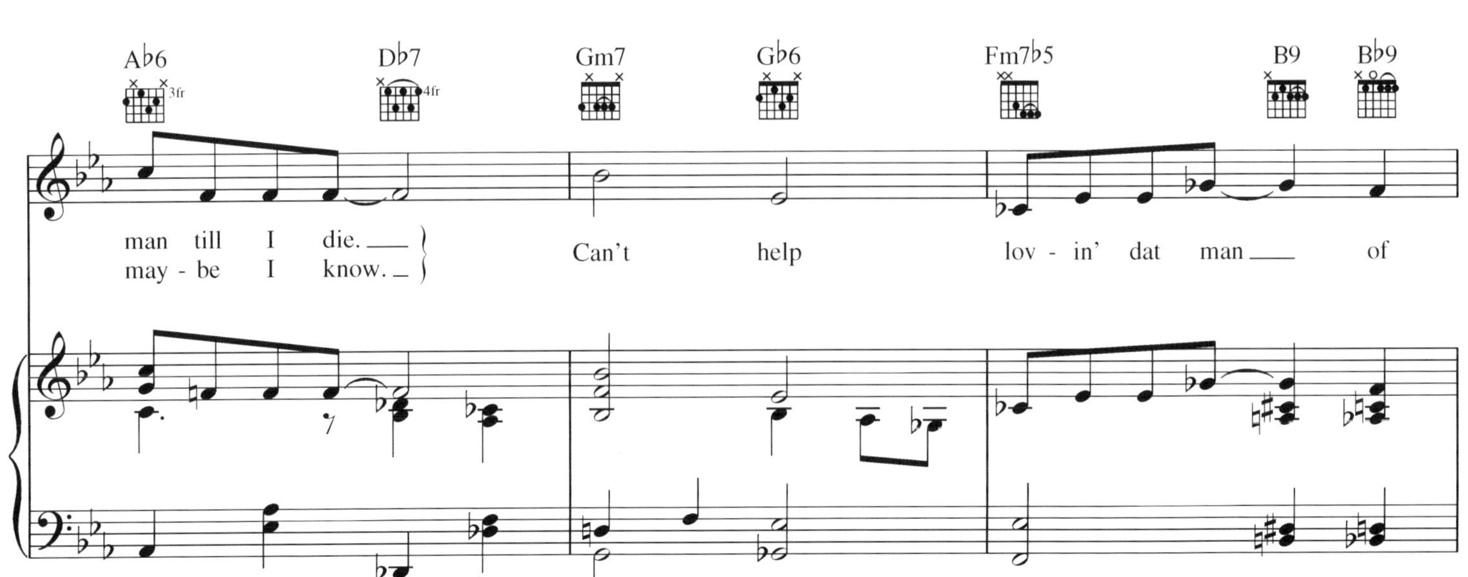

1
Eb6
Cm7
Abmaj7
Gm7
Fm7
E7
2
Eb6
Fm7
mine.
mine.
F#dim7
Eb/G
Ab6
Adim7
When he goes a - way
Eb/Bb
F7/C
Eb/Bb
dat's a rain - y day,
and when he comes
Ebdim7/Bb
Fm7/Bb
Bb7
back dat day is fine, de sun will shine.

E♭maj7
3fr
Cm7
3fr
Fm7
B♭7
He can come home as late as can be,
E♭maj7
3fr
E♭9
E♭7♭9
5fr
A♭6
3fr
D♭7
4fr
home wid - out him ain't no home to me.
Gm7
G♭6
Fm7♭5
B9
B♭9
1
E♭6
Can't help lov - in' dat man of mine.
G♭maj7
Fm7
E7
2
E♭6
mine.

CARAVAN
from SOPHISTICATED LADIES

Words and Music by DUKE ELLINGTON, IRVING MILLS and JUAN TIZOL

D♭dim C7 Fm6
4fr
on our car - a - van.
D♭dim C7 D♭dim C7 D♭dim C7
4fr 4fr 4fr
Sleep up - on my
D♭dim C7 D♭dim C7 D♭dim C7
4fr 4fr 4fr
shoul - der as we creep
D♭dim C7 D♭dim C7 D♭dim C7
4fr 4fr 4fr
a - cross the sands so I may keep

D♭dim
C7
D♭dim
C7
D♭dim
C7
this mem - 'ry of our car - a -
Fm6
van.
F7
F7♭9
F+
This is so ex - cit - ing
B♭7
Fm7/B♭
you are so in - vit -

Bb7
Eb7
ing rest - ing in my
Gdim7
Ab
arms as I thrill to
C7
Fm6/C
Cdim7
C7
the mag - ic charms of
Dbdim
C7
Dbdim
C7
Dbdim
C7
you, Be - side me

D♭dim
C7
4fr
here be - neath the blue
my dream of love is com - ing true
with - in our des - ert car - a - van.
Fm6
1
2

DANCING ON THE CEILING

Words by LORENZ HART
Music by RICHARD RODGERS

C7♭9
F
F/A
face I see.
At night I creep in bed
A♭dim7
Gm7
F
and nev - er sleep in bed,
but look a - bove in the
air,
Fm
F
C7
C7♭9
and to my great - est
joy,
my
boy
is
F
Am
D7
there!
It is my prince who
walks

Gm
3fr
C7
F
in - to my dreams and talks.
He danc - es
A+
B♭6
G7
C
Em
o - ver - head on the ceil - ing near my bed,
Gm7
C7
F
B♭6
C7
in my sight, through the
F
A+
night. I try to hide in vain

B♭6
G7
C
Em
Gm7
C7
un - der - neath my coun - ter - pane; there's my
F
B♭6
C7
F
love up a - bove!
C7
F6
I whis - per, "Go a - way, my lov - er; it's not fair."
C7
C7♭9
But I'm so grate - ful to dis - cov - er

F
Cdim7
C7
he's still there.
I love my
A+
B♭6
G7
C
Em
ceil - ing more since it is a danc - ing floor
Gm
3fr
C7
1
just for my love.
Gm7
C7
2
love.

THE COFFEE SONG
(They've Got An Awful Lot Of Coffee In Brazil)

Words and Music by BOB HILLIARD
and DICK MILES

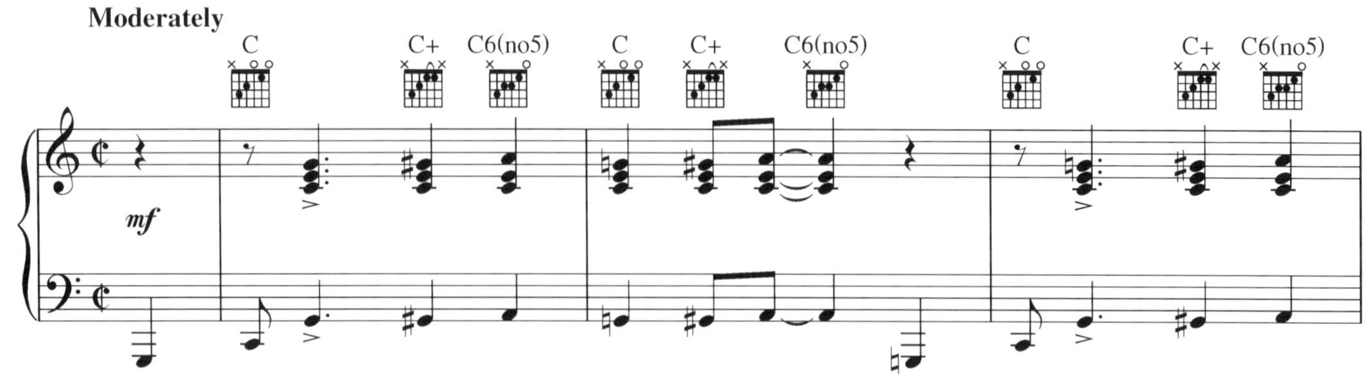

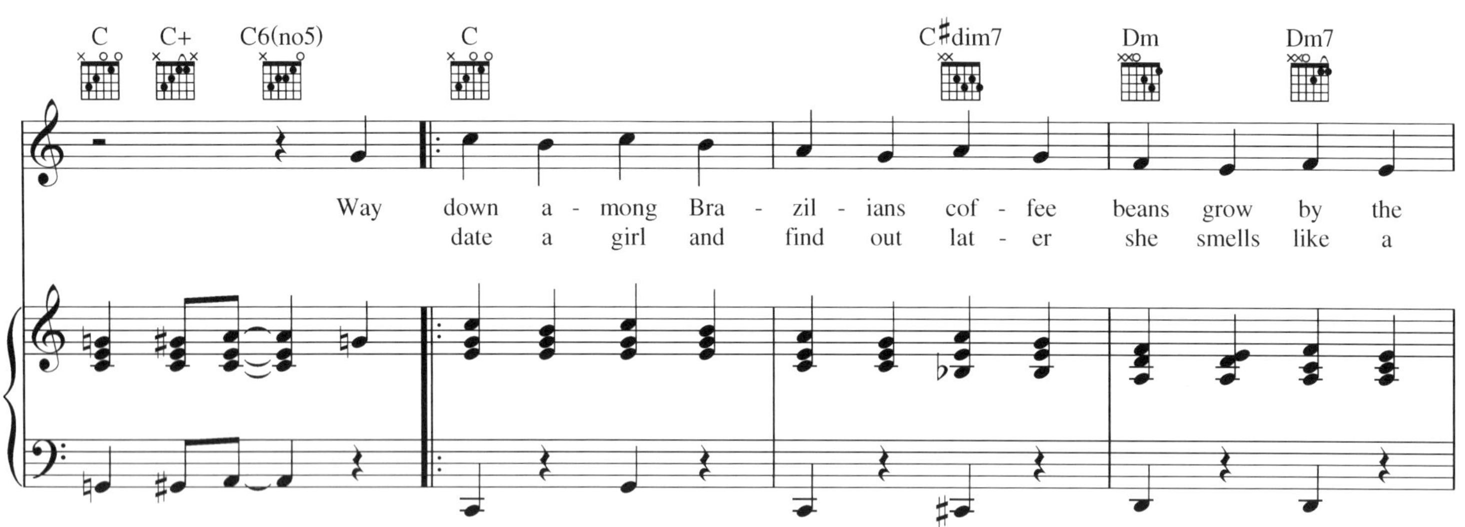

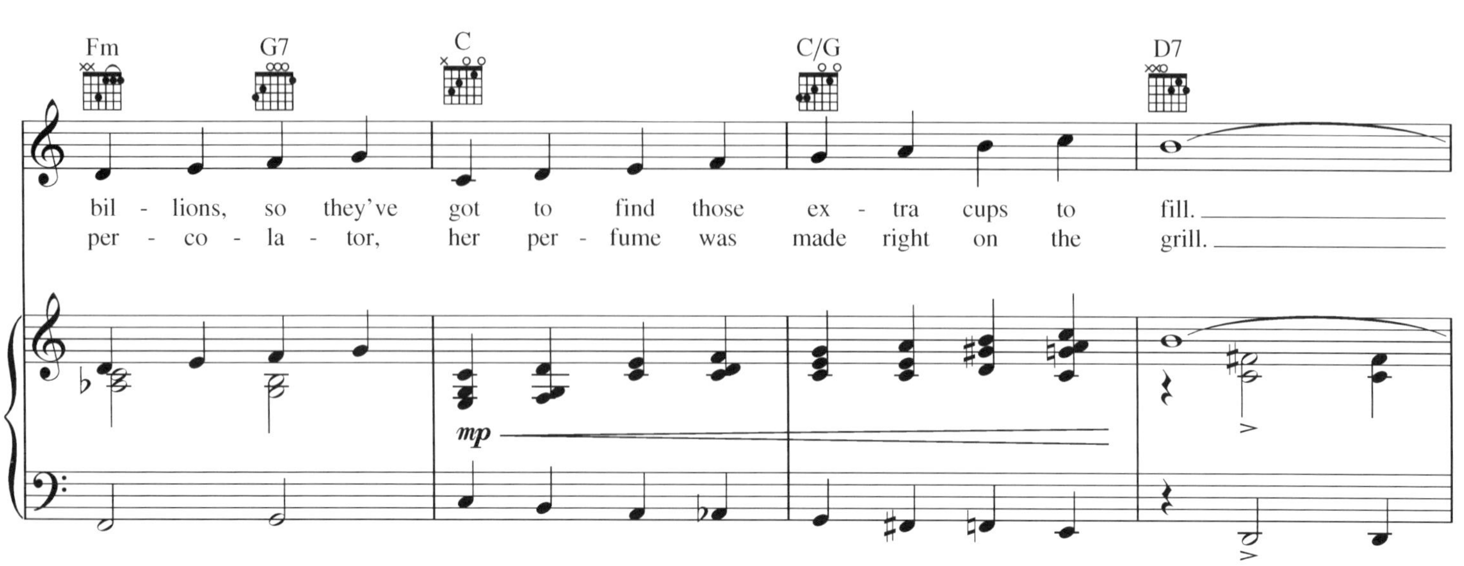

D♯dim
C/E
E♭dim
Dm9
G6/9
C
C+
C6(no5)
They've got an aw - ful lot of cof - fee in Bra - zil.
Why they could per - co - late the o - cean in Bra - zil.
C
C+
C6(no5)
C
C♯dim7
Dm
Dm7
You can't get cher - ry so - da 'cause they've got to sell their
And when their ham and eggs need sa - vor, cof - fee ketch - up
Fm
G7
C
C/G
D7
quo - ta, and the way things are I guess they nev - er will.
gives them fla - vor, cof - fee pick - les way out sell the dill.
mp
D♯dim7
C/E
E♭dim
Dm9
G6/9
C
C+
C6(no5)
They've got a zil - lion tons of cof - fee in Bra - zil.
Why they put cof - fee in the cof - fee in Bra - zil.

C C♯dim7 Dm7 G7 F/G G7 C

No tea or to - ma - to juice,

C♯dim7 Dm7 G7 F/G G7 C

you'll see no po - ta - to juice.

A7 Dm Am7 Am7/E E♭7 D7

'Cause the plant - ers down in San - tos all say No! No!

G7 C C♯dim7 Dm Dm7

No! { A pol - i - ti - cian's daugh - ter was ac - cused of drink - ing
{ So you'll add to the lo - cal col - or serv - ing cof - fee

Fm G7 C C/G
wa - ter and was fined a great big fif - ty dol - lar
with a crull - er, dunk - ing does - n't take a lot of
D7 Fm C/G Am7
bill.
skill.
They've got an aw - ful lot of
D9 D♭maj7 1 C C+ C6(no5) C C+ C6(no5) G7
cof - fee in Bra - zil.
You
2 C C+ C6(no5) C C+ C6(no5) C C+ C6(no5) C C+ C6(no5)
zil.

COME FLY WITH ME

Words by SAMMY CAHN
Music by JAMES VAN HEUSEN

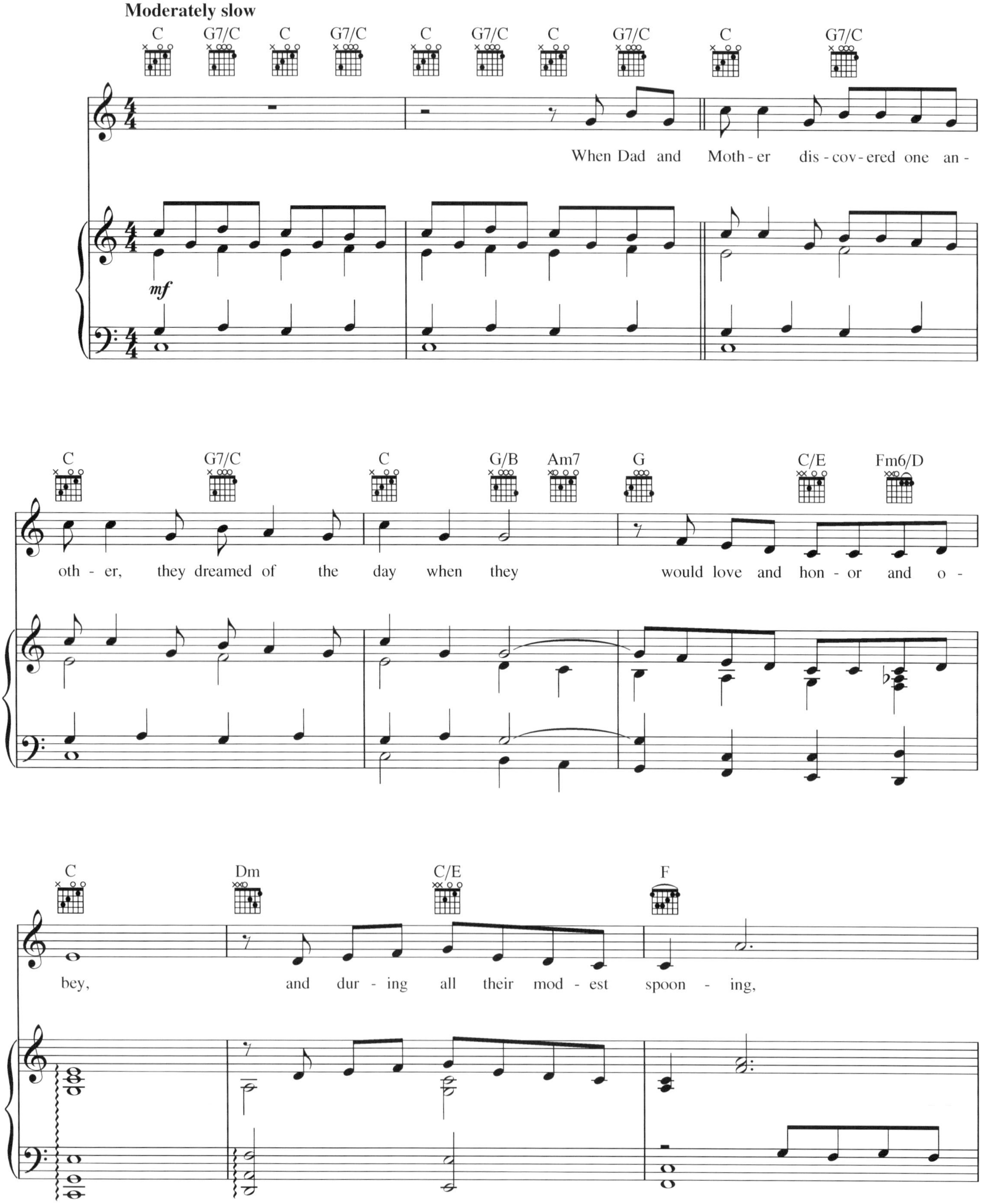

Moderately slow

C G7/C C G7/C C G7/C C G7/C C G7/C

mf

When Dad and Moth - er dis - cov - ered one an -

C G7/C C G/B Am7 G C/E Fm6/D

oth - er, they dreamed of the day when they would love and hon - or and o -

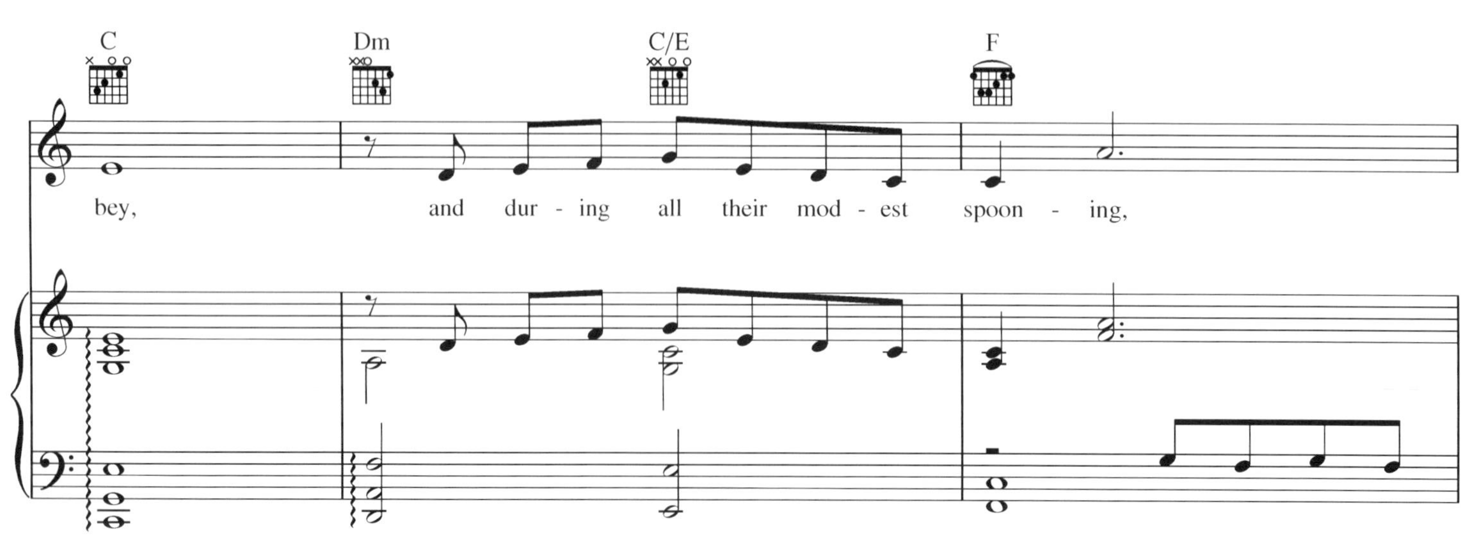

G
G/F
Em7
Am
C/G
they'd blush and speak of hon - ey - moon - ing.
And if your mem - o - ry re -
Am6/F♯
4fr
C/E
D7
F6/G
Fm6/G
G7
G7♯5
3
calls,
they spoke of Ni - ag - 'ra Falls.
But to -
C
G7/C
C
Am
E+
Am7
D13
4fr
day, my dar - ling, to - day,
when you meet the one you love,
you
Moderately, with a strong beat
G7
Cmaj9
C6
say:
Come fly with me!
Let's fly!

Cmaj9/E C6/E Edim7 Dm G7 C
Let's fly a - way! If you can use some ex -
Cmaj7 C7 Fmaj9 F6 B♭9
ot - ic booze, there's a bar in far Bom - bay. Come
(views,)
Cmaj7 C6/E F9 F/G G7 E7 A7
fly with me! Let's fly! Let's fly a - way!
D7 G7 Cmaj9 C6 Cmaj9/E C6/E Edim7 Dm
Come fly with me! Let's float down to Pe - ru!

G7
C
Cmaj7
C7
Fmaj9
F6
In lla - ma land there's a one - man band and he'll toot his flute for
B♭9
Cmaj7
C6/E
F9
F/G
G7
you. Come fly with me! Let's take off in the blue!
C
F7
C
A♭
4fr
A♭+
4fr
Once I get you up there, where the air is
D♭maj7
D♭6
B♭m
B♭m(maj7)
6fr
B♭m7
E♭7
rar - i - fied, we'll just glide,

A♭
A♭+
A♭6
D♭/A♭
4fr
4fr
3fr
4fr
star - ry - eyed. Once I get you up there, I'll be hold - ing
G
G♯m7♭5
G♯dim7
Am7
D7
you so near; you may hear
G7
Cmaj9
C6
an - gels cheer 'cause we're to - geth - er. Weath - er - wise, it's such
Cmaj9/E
C6/E
E♭dim
6fr
Dm
G7
a love - ly day! Just

C
Cmaj7
C7
Fmaj9
F6
F/C
say the words and we'll beat the birds down to A - ca - pul - co
B♭9
Cmaj7
C6/E
F9
F/G
G/F
Bay. It's per - fect for a fly - ing hon - ey -
Em7♭5
B♭7
A7
D7
Dm7
Dm7/G
G7
moon, they say. Come fly with me! Let's fly! Let's fly a -
1
2
C
Dm7
G7
C
way! Come way!

DAY BY DAY

Theme from the Paramount Television Series DAY BY DAY

Words and Music by SAMMY CAHN,
AXEL STORDAHL and PAUL WESTON

B7
Em
Em (maj7)
Em7
end to my de - vo - tion;
it's
A7
Em7
A7
Am7/D
deep - er, dear, by far than an - y o - cean.
D7♭9
4fr
E7♭9
Am7
I find that day by day
you're mak - ing
D7
G
all my dreams come true.
So come what may

Bm7♭5
E7
I want you to know
I'm
Am7
D7
G
Bm7♭5/F
yours a - lone
and I'm in love to
E7
E7♭9
Am7
D9
D7♭9
4fr
stay, as we go through the years, day by
G6
Am7
D9
C
G
day.
day.
rall.

A DAY IN THE LIFE OF A FOOL
(Manhã De Carnaval)

Words by CARL SIGMAN
Music by LUIZ BONFA

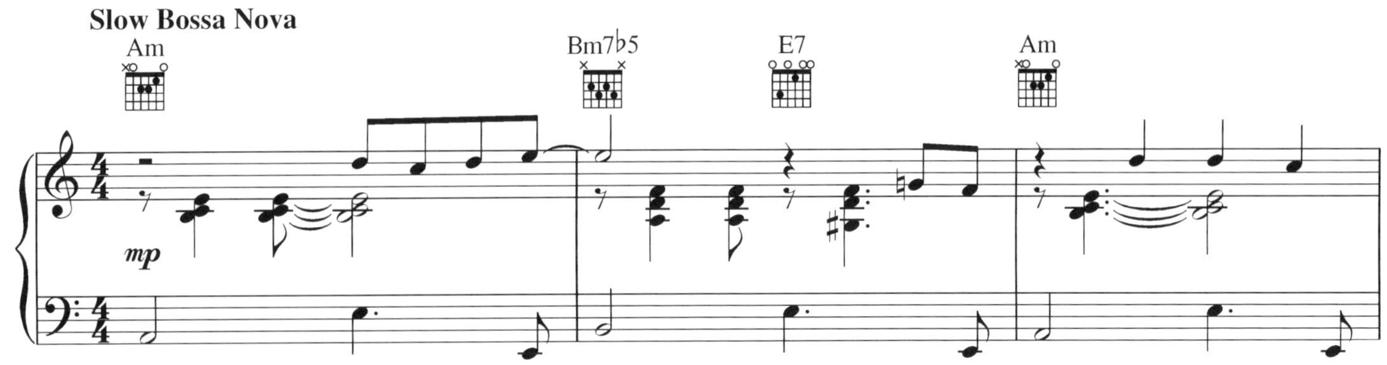

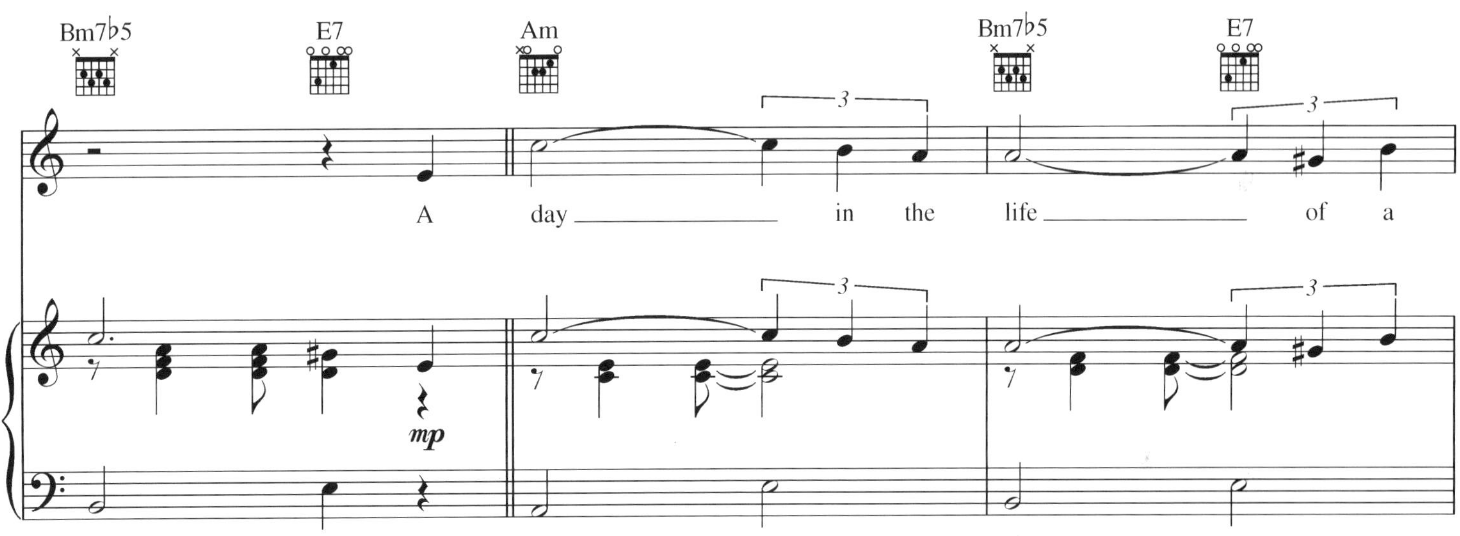

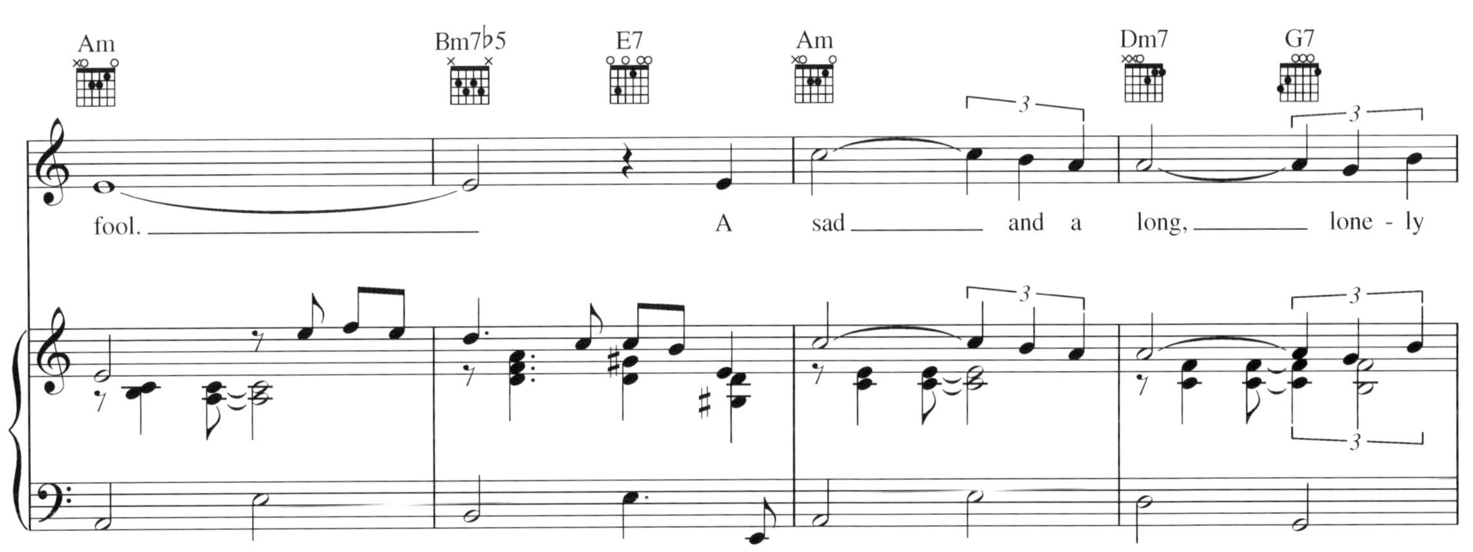

Cmaj7
C6
Dm7
G7
day.
I walk the av - e - nue
and hope I'll
Cmaj7
C6
Fmaj7
Bm7♭5
E7
run in - to
The wel-come sight of you
com - ing my
Am
Bm7♭5
E7
Am
Bm7♭5
E7
way.
I stop just a - cross
from your
Am
Bm7♭5
E7
A7sus
A7♭9
door,
but you're nev - er home
an - y -

Dm
Bm7♭5
E7♭5
more.
So back to my room
Am
Dm6/F
Bm7♭5
E7
Rubato
and there in the gloom I cry
tears of good-
Am
Dm7
Am
Dm7
Am7
Dm7
Am7
bye.
'Til you come back to me, that's the way it will be ev - 'ry
Dm7
Em7
Am
Repeat and Fade
Optional Ending
day in the life of a fool.
8va
8va
a tempo

DEARLY BELOVED

from YOU WERE NEVER LOVELIER

Music by JEROME KERN
Words by JOHNNY MERCER

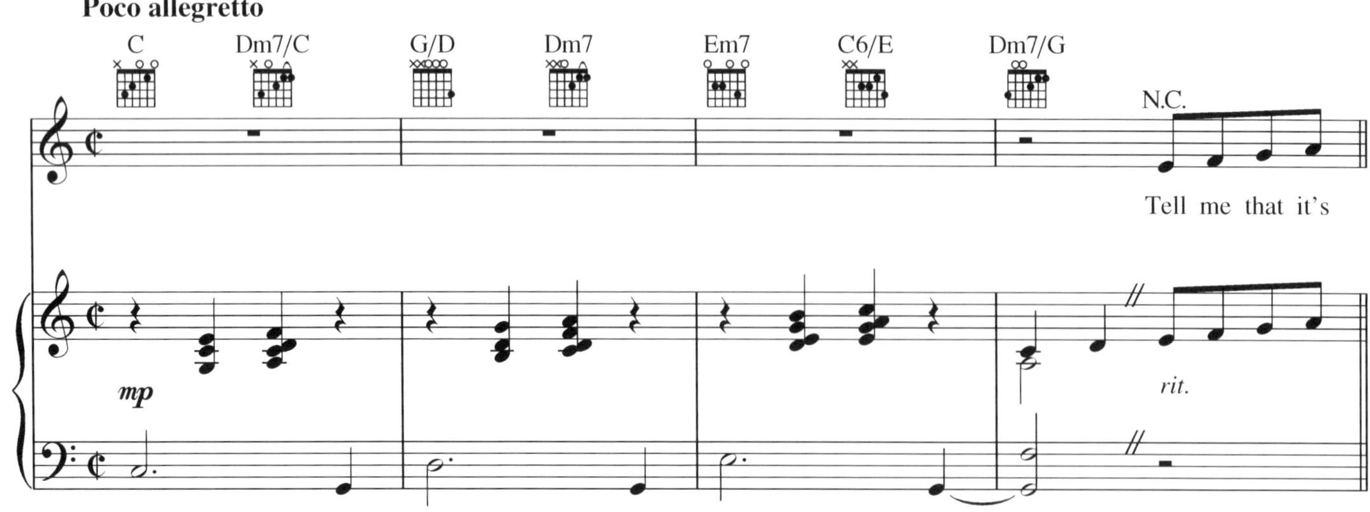

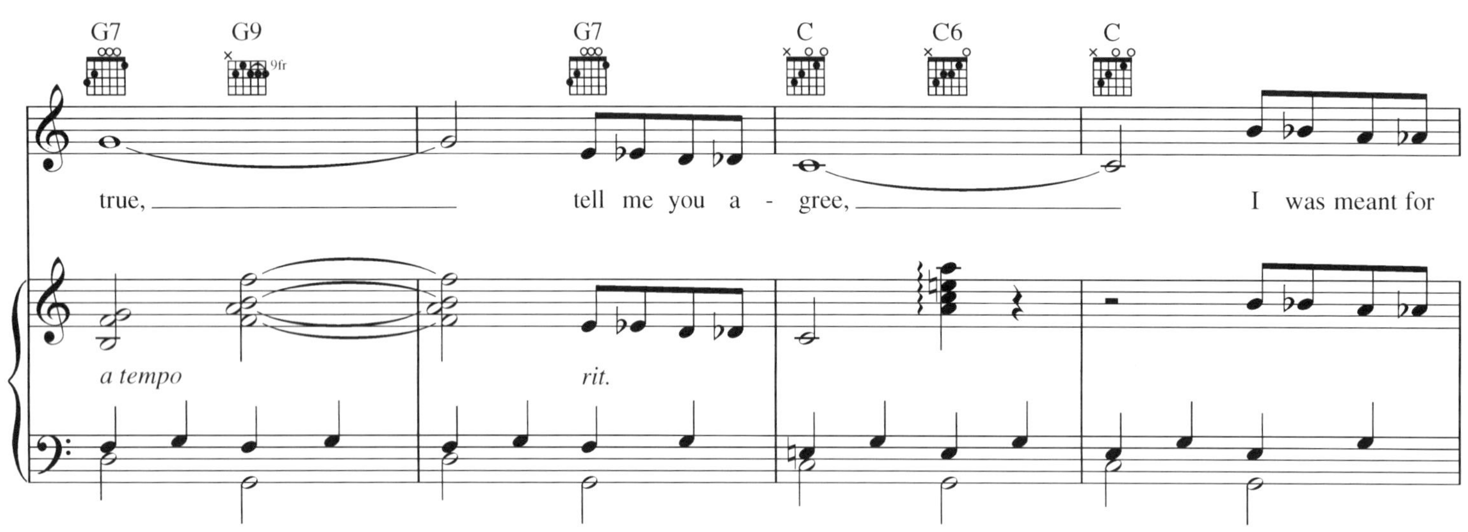

G
F/A
G/B
F/A
Dear - ly be - lov - ed, how clear - ly I see,
G/B
F/A
Dm7
G
G9/F
some - where in Heav - en you were fash - ioned for me.
C/E
Dm7
G7/D
Dm7/G
G7
An - gel eyes knew you,
Cmaj7
Gdim
C6
Em
A♭9
A♭7
4fr
an - gel voic - es led me to you;

G
F/A
G/B
F/A
noth - ing could save me, fate gave me a sign.
G/B
F/A
Dm7
G
Bdim/F
I know that I'll be yours come show - er or shine;
C/E
D7
G7
Gdim
so I say merely, dear - ly be-
rall. e dim.
Dm7
G7
1
C
B♭7
2
C
lov - ed, be mine. mine.
a tempo

DESAFINADO
(Off Key)

English Lyric by GENE LEES
Original Text by NEWTON MENDONÇA
Music by ANTONIO CARLOS JOBIM

Bossa Nova tempo
Amaj7 Ab7#5 G Gb7b5 F
When I come a-round, must you al-ways put me down? If you say my sing-
Se vo-cê dis-ser
mf
G7b5
-ing is off key, my love,
que eu de-sa-fi no a-mor,
Gm7 C7 Am7b5
you will hurt my feel-ings, don't you see, my love?
sai-ba que is-to em mim pro-vo-ca i-men-sa dôr.
3
D7b9 Gm7 A7b9
I wish I had an ear like yours, a voice
Só pri-vi-le-gi-a-dos têm ou-vi-

Dmaj7
D7♭9
4 fr
G7
that would be - have.
All I have is feel -
- do i - gual ão seu.
Eu po - ssuo a pe -
Gbmaj7
Gb7b5
ing and the voice God gave.
- nas o que Deus me deu.
3
F
G7♭5
You in - sist my mu - sic goes a - gainst the rules.
Se vo - cê in - sis - te em cla - ssi - fi - car,
Gm7
3 fr
C7
Yes, but rules were nev - er made for love -
o meu com - por - ta - men - to de an - ti mu -

Am7♭5
D7♭9
4 fr
Gm7
3 fr
- sick fools; I wrote this lit - tle song
- si - cal. Eu mes - mo men - tin -
3
A7♯5
Dm7
E7
for you, but you don't care.
- do po - sso ar - gu - men - tar,
Amaj7
A♭7♯5
G
It's a crook - ed song, ah, but all my heart is there.
que is to é bo - ssa no - va, que is - to é mui - to na - tu - ral.
G♭7
Amaj7
A♯dim7
The thing that you would see if you would play
O que vo - cê não sa - be nem se quer

Bm7
2 fr
E7♭9
Amaj7
your part is e - ven if I'm out
pre - ssente, é que os de - sa - fi - na -
Am7
Bm7♭5
B♭7♭5
of tune I have a gen - tle heart. I took
- dos tam - bem têm co - ra - ção. Fo - to -
Cmaj7
C#dim7
Dm7
your pic - ture with my trust - y Rol - lei - flex.
- gra - fei vo - cê na mi - nha Rol - lei - flex.
G13
2 fr
Gm7
3 fr
E♭m6
And now all I have de - vel - oped is a com -
Re - ve - lou - se a su - a e - nor me in - gra - ti - dão.

Gm7
3 fr
C7♭9
F
- plex.
Pos - si - bly in vain,
Só não po - de - rá
G7♭5
I hope you weak - en, oh my love.
fa - lar a - ssim do meu a - mor.
Gm7
3 fr
C7
And for - get those rig - id rules that un -
É - le é o ma - ior que vo - cê po -
Am7♭5
D7♭9
4 fr
B♭maj7
- der - mine my dream of a life of love and mu -
- de en - con - trar "viu." Vo - cê com a sua mú -

B♭m6
Am7
A♭dim7
-sic with __ some - one __ who'll un - der - stand. __ That e - ven
- si - ca es __ que ceu __ o prin - ci - pal. __ É que no
G7
G♭maj7
though I may be out of tune __ when I at - tempt to say how much I love __
pei - to dos de - sa - fi - na - dos no fun - do do pei - to ba - te ca - la -
G7
you, __ all that mat - ters is the mes - sage that I
- do, __ é que no pei - to dos de - sa - fi - na -
Gm7
C7
F
C7♭9
F6
Fmaj7♯11
bring, which is: __ My dear __ one, I love you.
- dos tam - bém ba - te um co - ra - ção!

DEVIL MAY CARE

Words and Music by BOB DOROUGH
and TERRELL P. KIRK, JR.

Original key: Bb minor. This edition has been transposed up one whole step to be more playable.

Cm
3fr
Am7♭5
Dm7
G7
Cm
3fr
as I can be. I've learned to love and to live,
Am7♭5
D7♯9(♭13)
5fr
G7♯9(♭13)
9fr
Cm
3fr
Am7♭5
dev - il may care. No cares and
Dm7
G7
Cm
3fr
Am7♭5
Dm7
G7
3
woes; what - ev - er comes lat - er goes. That's how I'll
3
Dm7♭5
G7♯9(♭13)
9fr
Cm
3fr
take and I'll give, dev - il may care.

Fm7
Bb7sus
Bb7
When the day is through, I suf - fer
Ebmaj7
Ab7#11
Gm7
C7#9(b13)
Fm7
no re - grets. I know that he who threats
Bb7b9
Ebmaj7
Ebm9
los - es a night. For on - ly a fool
Ab13
Db
thinks he can hold back the dawn. He who is

Dm7♭5
G7♯9(♭13)
Cmaj7
wise nev - er tries to re - vise what's past and gone.
Dm7♭5
G7♯9(♭13)
Cm
Am7♭5
D7
G7
Live love to - day; let come to -
Cm
Am7♭5
D7
G7
Cm
- mor - row what may. Don't e - ven stop for a sigh;
Am7♭5
A♭13
it does - n't help if you cry. That's how I'll

1, 2
Dm7♭5
G7♯9(♭13)
9fr
Cm
3fr
live and I'll die, dev - il may care.
3
Cm
3fr
Am7♭5
A♭7
4fr
G7♯9(♭13)
9fr
Cm
3fr
Am7♭5
A♭7
4fr
care. Dev - il may care. Sure -
G7♯9(♭13)
9fr
Cm
3fr
Am7♭5
A♭7
4fr
G7
3
- ly dev - il may care. Dev - il may care.
3
Cm
3fr
B♭m
A♭maj9
3fr
G7♯9(♭13)
9fr
Cm(maj7)♯11
8fr

DO NOTHIN' TILL YOU HEAR FROM ME

Words and Music by DUKE ELLINGTON
and BOB RUSSELL

G
Gmaj7/D
G7
Cmaj7
me.
At least con - sid - er our ro - mance.
Cm
G
Am7
D9
G
If you should take the word of oth - ers you've heard,
I have - n't a chance.
Am7
G
Cm
E♭
E♭maj7
True I've been seen
E♭
E♭maj7
E♭
E♭maj7
E♭
E♭9
with some - one new, but does that mean that I'm un - true. When we're a -

Am7
D7
G
E9
Gm
3fr
D
A7
D7
part, the words in my heart re - veal how I feel a - bout you.
N.C.
G
Gmaj7
G7
Cmaj7
Some kiss may cloud my mem - o - ry, and oth - er arms may hold a thrill.
Cm
3fr
G
Am7
D9
4fr
G
But please do noth - in' till you hear it from me, and you nev - er will.
1
B♭7
E♭9
D9
4fr
N.C.
Do noth - in' till you hear from
2
G
C
Cm
3fr
G

DON'T BLAME ME

Words by DOROTHY FIELDS
Music by JIMMY McHUGH

C G7 C G7 Cmaj7 C6
school. My poor heart is in an aw - ful state now, but it's too
team. Ev - er since the hour of our meet - ing I've been re -
Cmaj7 C6 A9 D7 D7♯5
late now to call a halt, so if I be - come a
peat - ing a sil - ly phrase hop - ing that you'll un - der -
Gmaj7 G7 Am D7 G7
nui - sance it's all your fault!
stand me one of these days.
dim.
rit.
C/E B♭/D A/C♯ A7 Dm7♭5 G13
2fr
3
Don't blame me for fall - ing in love with
p-f

Cmaj9 C6 Dm7♭5 G7 Em7♭5 A7
you, I'm un - der your spell but how can I help it,
Dm7 G+ C G7 C/E B♭/D
don't blame me! Can't you
A/C♯ A7 Dm7♭5 G13 Cmaj9 C6 Dm7♭5 G7
see when you do the things you do! If I can't con - ceal the
Em7♭5 A7 Dm7 G7 G7♯5 C Fm6 Cdim7 C7 F
thrill that I'm feel - ing, don't blame me. I can't help it
cresc.

E7
Am
D7
if that dog - goned moon a - bove
makes me need
Dm7/G
Dm7♭5
G7
C/E
B♭/D
some - one like you to love!
Blame your
A/C♯
A7
Dm7♭5
G13
2fr
Cmaj9
C6
Dm7♭5
G7
kiss, as sweet as a kiss can be
and blame all your charms that
Em7♭5
A7
Dm7
G7sus
1 C
G7
2 C
melt in my arms, but don't blame me.
me.

DON'T GET AROUND MUCH ANYMORE

from SOPHISTICATED LADY

Words and Music by DUKE ELLINGTON
and BOB RUSSELL

N.C.
C
Thought I'd vis - it the club,
got as far as the
A7
Am7
D7
door,
they'd have ask'd me a - bout you,
G7
C
F
Fm7
don't get a - round much an - y - more.
Dar - ling, I guess
Cmaj7
C7
C7♯5
8fr
F
my mind's more at ease,
but nev - er - the - less,

F♯dim
G7
F♯dim
G7
N.C.
C
why stir up mem - o - ries? Been in - vit - ed on dates,
A7
Am7
D7
might have gone, but what for? Aw - f'lly dif - f'rent with - out you,
G7
1
C
don't get a - round much an - y - more. Missed the Sat - ur - day
2
C
N.C.
C7♯9
more.

DREAMSVILLE

Lyrics by JAY LIVINGSTON and RAY EVANS
Music by HENRY MANCINI

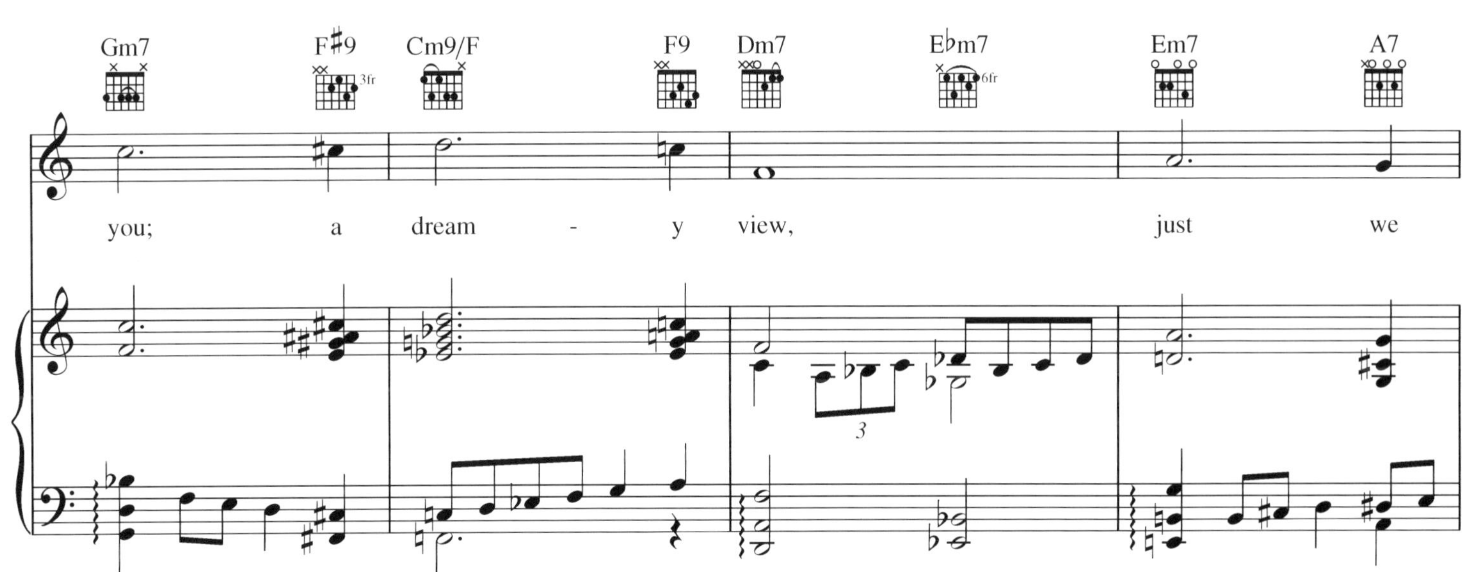

Dm7
G7♭9
Cmaj9
Gm7/C
Cmaj9
two a - lone with love in Dreams-ville. _ Time is
Gm7
F♯9
3fr
Cm9/F
F9
Dm7
E♭m7
6fr
Dm9
3fr
D♭9♯11
new; we're here to love and we
Cmaj9
F♯m7♭5
4fr
B7♭9
Em9
A7♭9
5fr
do. We can see the rest of the world be - low us from
F♯m7
D
F9
G♯m7♭5
C♯9
our pink cloud. There's no boun - d'ry to this

F♯m7♭5
B7♭9
Em7♭5
A7
Dm7
G7♭9
mag - ic land
as we go ex - plor - ing
hand in hand in
Cmaj9
Gm7/C
Cmaj9
Gm7
F♯9
dream - y Dreams-ville,
far a - way,
and
Cm9/F
F9
Dm7
E♭m7
Dm9
D♭9♯11
here we love,
here we'll
Cmaj9
Dm9
D♭9♯11
Cmaj9
stay.
here we'll stay.
rit.

EAST OF THE SUN
(And West Of The Moon)

Words and Music by
BROOKS BOWMAN

D9
F♯7/C♯
B7
Em
A7
day, near to the moon at night, we'll live in a love - ly
Am7
D9
D7
G
Gmaj7
way, dear, liv - ing on love and pale moon - light. Just you and I,
G6
G
F7♭5
E9
for - ev - er and a day;
Am7
Am9
C6
Cm/A
love will not die, we'll keep it that way.

Am7
Cm(maj7)/A
Cm
3fr
Up a - mong the stars we'll find, A
G
Em
A7
Am
Cm6
D9
har - mo - ny of life to a love - ly tune, east of the sun and west of the
G
E♭7
Am7
D9
D7
moon, dear, east of the sun and west of the
1
G
Am7
D7
moon.
2
G
Am7
A♭maj7
Gmaj7
moon.
rit.

EASY LIVING

Theme from the Paramount Picture EASY LIVING

Words and Music by LEO ROBIN
and RALPH RAINGER

Fm Bb7 Eb Cm Ab Abm
the years I'm giv - ing, They're eas - y to give When you're in love I'm
Eb C7 Fm Bb9 Bb7b9 Eb Ab
hap - py to do what - ev - er I do for you,
Eb Ab Eb Cb Gb7
for you. May - be I'm a fool but it's fun.
Cb Gb7 Cb
Peo - ple say you rule me with one wave of your hand.
cresc. poco a poco

A♭m
Fdim7
B♭7sus
B♭7
Fm7
B♭7
B♭9♯5
Dar - ling, it's grand
They just don't un - der - stand.
mf - f
E♭
Edim
Fm
B♭7
E♭
Cm
Liv - ing for you
Is eas - y liv - ing, It's eas - y to live
A♭
A♭m
E♭
C7
Fm
B♭9
B♭7♭9
When you're in love and I'm so in love, there's noth - ing in life but
E♭
Fm
E♭
B9
B♭7sus
B♭7
B♭7♯5
E♭
Fm
E♭
A♭
E♭
B♭9♯5
E♭6
you.
you.
rit.

FALLING IN LOVE WITH LOVE

from THE BOYS FROM SYRACUSE

Words by LORENZ HART
Music by RICHARD RODGERS

F7sus
Cm7
3fr
F7
la - dies, let your fin - gers dance,
mf
And
F7sus
Cm7
3fr
F7
keep your hands out of ro - mance.
Love - ly

Bb/D
G7b9
Cm7
F7
witch - es, let the stitch - es Keep your
Cm7
F7
Bb
fin - gers un - der con - trol. Cut the
Gm
Cm
thread, but leave The
Cm7
F7
Bb
whole heart whole.

F7
Mer - ry maids can sew and sleep,
Cm7/F
Fdim7
F7
Wives can on - ly sew and weep!
B♭
B♭maj7
B♭6
B♭
Fall - ing in love with love Is fall - ing for

F7sus
F7
Cm7
3fr
F7
make be - lieve.
F7sus
F7
F7sus
F7
Fall - ing in love with love Is play - ing the
B♭maj7
B♭6
B♭maj7
B♭6
fool;
B♭maj7
B♭6
B♭maj7
B♭6
Car - ing too much is such a ju - ve - nile

Am7
D7
F6/A
D7
fan - cy.
Gdim7
Gm
3fr
Cm/G
3fr
C7/G
Learn - ing to trust is just For chil - dren in
Cm7/F
Cm7
3fr
F7
school.
B♭
B♭maj7
B♭6
B♭
I fell in love with love one night When the

F7sus
F7
Cm7
3fr
F7
moon was full,
F7sus
F7
F7sus
F7
I was un - wise with eyes Un - a - ble to
B♭maj7
B♭6
B♭maj7
B♭6
see.
B♭maj7
B♭6
B♭maj7
B♭6
I fell in love with love, With love ev - er -

Am7
D7
Gmaj7
G7
last - ing,
But
Cm/E♭
Ddim7
Cm7
F7
love
fell
out
with
1
B♭
F7
me.
2
B♭
B♭6
me.
Ped.

FEELS SO GOOD

Dm
Bm7♭5
be - cause I need - ed just to hear that
E7♯5
E7
Am
B♭maj7
spe - cial some - thing.
Am
B♭maj7
C
B♭
And then one day you just ap - peared,

Am
you said "Hel - lo
let's make love a - long the
Fmaj7
Dm
way."
Your name is mu - sic to my heart;
Dm7
Em7
Fmaj7
F♯dim
9fr
G
I'll al - ways real - ly
C
To Coda
C
Bdim
E♭m/B♭
6fr
Em/A
A7♭9
5fr
A7/B
C♯dim7
Dm7
love you.
Feels so good when I'm with you.

Dm
Dm/G
C
I can't be - lieve you love me too.
C
Bdim
E♭m/B♭
Em/A
A7♭9
A7/B
C♯dim7
Dm7
With you it feels like it should feel.
Fmaj7/G
F/G
D.S. al Coda
Feels so good.
CODA
C
Bdim
E♭m/B♭
Em/A
A7♭9
A7/B
C♯dim7
Dm7
Feels so good when I'm with you.
I'll trade my base - ball cards for you.

F/G
C
I can't be - lieve you love me too.
Now I be - lieve that dreams come true.
C
Bdim
E♭m/B♭
Em/B
A7♭9
A7/B
C♯dim7
Dm7
With you it feels like it should feel.
With you my smile sticks all the time.
Repeat and Fade
Feels so good. Let's make a deal
With you the sun will al - ways shine
Optional Ending
Fmaj7/G
With you it feels so good.

FINE AND MELLOW

Words and Music by
BILLIE HOLIDAY

C7
C9
D♭9
C9
F
Gm7
C7
low - est man
that I've
ev - er
seen.
F
D♭9
C7
C7♯5
Fm6
B♭7
B♭9
He wears
high
draped
pants,
stripes
are
real - ly
yel -
F
Gm7
F/A
Gm7
F
D♭dim
F7/C
F9
B♭
low.
He wears
high
draped
pants,
B♭9
F
C7
F
F♯dim
stripes
are
real - ly
yel - low.
But when he

Gm7
C9
D♭9
C9
F
starts in to love me he's so fine and mel - low.
Fm
Fm6
B♭
B♭7
Love will make you drink and gam - ble, make you stay out all night
F
C7
F7/A
F9
B♭
long.
Love will make you drink and gam - ble,
B♭9
F
C7/G
F/A
F6
make you stay out all night long.

C9♯5
C9
D♭9
C9
F
Gm7
C7
Love will make you do things that you know is wrong.
3
3
F
Cm7
C7
3fr
F6
N.C.
F6
N.C.
But if you treat me right ba - by,
I'll stay home ev - 'ry
F
C7/G
F/A
C7/G
F
D♭dim
F7/C
F7
B♭
day.
If you treat me right ba - by,
B♭9
F
Fm6
I'll stay home ev - 'ry day.
But you're so

C7♯5 C7
D♭9
C9
F
Gm7 C7
F D♭9/A♭ C7/G C9♯5
mean to me ba-by I know you're gon - na drive me a - way. Love is
Fm6
Fm
B♭
B♭9
F
C/G
F7/A
F7
just like a fau - cet, it turns off and on.
B♭
B♭7
B♭9
F
C7/G
F/A
F♯dim
Love is like a fau - cet, it turns off and on. Some - times when you
Gm7
C7
D♭9
C9
F6 E♭
D♭9 C9
F G♭9 F9
think it's on ba - by, it has turned off and gone.

A FINE ROMANCE

from SWING TIME

Words by DOROTHY FIELDS
Music by JEROME KERN

E♭dim7
Dm7
G7
Dm7
G7
cou - ple of hot to - ma - toes, but
seals in the Arc - tic O - cean; at
C
E7
you're as cold as yes - ter - day's mashed po - ta - toes.
least they flap their fins to ex - press e - mo - tion.
Dm7
G7
C
C♯dim7
G7/D
A fine ro - mance; you won't
A fine ro - mance, with no
G7♯5
C
G7
nes - tle! A fine ro - mance; you won't
quar - rels, with no in - sults, and all

C
A7
wres - tle! I might as well play bridge with my old maid
mor - als! I've nev - er mussed the crease in your blue serge
Dm
A7/E
F
F♯dim7
C/G
aunts! I have - n't got a chance.
pants; I nev - er get the chance.
G7
1
C
Dm7
G7
This is a fine ro - mance!
This is a fine ro -
C
Dm7
G7
2
C
G7
A mance!

C/G
Dm7/G
G9/D
9fr
C
B7/D♯
3
G7/D
Dm7/G
G7
C
Male: A
fine
ro - mance,
with
fine
ro - mance,
my
G7
G7♯5
C
no
kiss - es!
A
fine
ro - mance,
my
dear
Duch - ess!
Two
old
fo - gies
who
G7
C/E
friend,
this
is!
We
two
should
be
like
need
crutch - es!
True
love
should
have
the

E♭dim7
Dm7
G7
Dm7
G7
clams in a dish of chow - der, but
thrills that a health - y crime has. We
3
C
E7
we just fizz like parts of a Seid - litz pow - der.
don't have half the thrills that the "March of Time" has.
Dm7
G7
C
C♯dim7
G7/D
A fine ro - mance, with no
A fine ro - mance, my good
G7♯5
C
G7
clinch - es! A fine ro - mance, with no
wom - an, my strong, "aged in the wood"

C
A7
pinch - es! You're just as hard to land as the "Île - de -
wom - an! You nev - er give the or - chids I send a
Dm
A7/E
F
F♯dim7
C/G
France! I have - n't got a chance.
glance. No! You like cac - tus plants.
G7
1
C
Dm7
G7
This is a fine ro - mance!
This is a fine ro -
C
Dm7
G7
2
C
A mance!

FLY ME TO THE MOON
(In Other Words)
featured in the Motion Picture ONCE AROUND

Words and Music by
BART HOWARD

Am7♭5
B♭7♯5
6fr
Gm7
C7
hold my hand! In
Fm7
A♭/B♭
4fr
B♭7♯5
6fr
A♭dim
3fr
E♭6
Dm7
G7♭9
oth - er words, dar - ling, kiss me!
3
3
Cm7
3fr
Fm7
B♭7
E♭maj7
3fr
Fill my heart with song, and let me sing for - ev - er - more;
A♭
4fr
Dm7♭5
G7♭9
Cm
3fr
C7
You are all I long for, all I wor - ship and a - dore. In

Fm7
A♭/B♭
D7♭9
1
Gm7♭5
C9
Cmaj7
oth - er words, please be true! In
Fm7
A♭/B♭
B♭9
E♭(add9)
oth - er words, I love you.
2
Gm7♭5
C9
C7♯5(♯9)
Fm7
A♭/B♭
true! In oth - er words,
B♭9
B♭7♭9
E♭6
N.C.
I love you!
8vb

GIRL TALK

from the Paramount Picture HARLOW

Words by BOBBY TROUP
Music by NEAL HEFTI

Am7
D7♭9
Am7
B♭m
Cm6
D7
Dm7/G
G9
be - comes es - sen - tial things that wom - en find so "ap - pro - po".
But that's a dame, {they're / we're} all the same
Gm7/C
B♭m7
Am7
Dm9
Gm7
C9
it's just a game. {They / We} call it Girl Talk, Girl Talk.
Fmaj7
B9
B♭maj9
Gm7
C7♭9
{They / We} all me - ow a - bout the ups and downs of all {their / our} friends,
Am7
D7♭9
Gm7
Am7
B♭
C9sus
Fm7
B♭m7
the "who," the "how," the "why," {they / we} dish the dirt, it nev - er ends.
The weak - er sex, the speak - er

G7♭5(♭9) Gm7/C C7♭9 Am7 D7♭9 Am7 B♭m Cm D7
sex { we / you } mor - tal males be - hold, but tho' we joke we would - n't trade you for a ton of gold.
Dm7/G G9 Gm7/C B♭m7
So ba - by stay and gab a - way, but hear me say that af - ter
(It's all been planned, so take my hand, please un - der - stand the sweet - est
Am7 Dm9 Gm7 C7♭9 F D7
Girl Talk, talk to me.
Girl Talk talks of you.)
Gm7 C9sus C9 F Am7 B♭maj9 Bm7♭5 C9sus Fmaj9
me.
you.)
8va

THE FRIM FRAM SAUCE

Words and Music by JOE RICARDEL
and REDD EVANS

A♭7 Adim7 E♭/B♭ C7 F7 B♭7
frim fram sauce with the oss and fay, with shi - fa - fa on the side.
E♭ C7 Fm7 B♭7sus E♭ C7
I don't want pork chops and ba - con; that won't a - wak - en
F7 B♭m7 A7 A♭7 Adim7
my ap - pe - tite in - side. I want the frim fram sauce with the
E♭/B♭ C7 Fm7 B♭7♭9 E♭
oss and fay with shi - fa - fa on the side. Well, you know a

Bbm7
Eb7
Abmaj7
F7
Bbm7
Eb7
girl, she real - ly got to eat, and a girl, she should eat right.
Abmaj7
Cm7
3fr
F7
Bbmaj7
G7b9
Five will get you ten; I'm gon - na
Cm7
3fr
F7
Bb7
Eb
3fr
feed my - self right to - night. I don't want fish cakes and rye bread;
C7
F7
C7
F7
you heard what I said. Wait - er, please, I want mine fried. I want the

A♭7
Adim7
E♭/B♭
C7
Fm7
B♭7
frim fram sauce with the oss and fay, with shi - fa - fa on the side.
1-3
E♭
4
Cm7 Bm7 B♭m7 A13 A♭9 Adim7
(4.) I don't want
Gm7 B/D♯ Fm11 B♭7♯9(♭13)
E♭6/9
Mm, with shi - fa - fa on the side.
8va
8vb

GEORGIA ON MY MIND

Words by STUART GORRELL
Music by HOAGY CARMICHAEL

A7
D7
D7♯5
D7
G9
9fr
C7
blos - soms fall and all the world's a song,
F
A7♯5
A7/D
Dm
G7
Edim7
C13
2fr
F
I'll go back to Geor - gia 'cause that's where I be - long.
F
A7
Dm
Geor - gia, Geor - gia, the whole day
Gm
3fr
B♭m
F
E7
Gm
3fr
G9
9fr
C7
F
F♯dim
9fr
through. Just an old sweet song keeps Geor - gia on my mind.

Gm7
C7♯5
8fr
F
A7
(Geor - gia on my mind.) Geor - gia, Geor - gia,
Dm
Gm
3fr
B♭m
F
E7
a song of you comes as sweet and clear as
Gm
3fr
G9
9fr
C13
2fr
F
E♭9
F
A7
Dm
Gm6
3fr
moon - light through the pines. Oth - er arms reach
Dm
B♭7
Dm
Gm6
3fr
Dm7
G7
out to me; Oth - er eyes smile ten - der - ly;

Dm
Gm6
Dm7
E7
Am
F♯dim
Fm6
Still in peace - ful dreams I see the road leads back to
Dm
C7
F
A7
Dm
you. Geor - gia, Geor - gia, no peace I
Gm
B♭m
F
E7
Gm
G9
C13
find. Just an old sweet song keeps Geor - gia on my
1
F
Dm
Gm7
C13
C7♯5
mind.
2
F
B♭6/9
C7♯5
F6
mind.
rit.

THE GIRL FROM IPANEMA
(Garôta De Ipanema)

Music by ANTONIO CARLOS JOBIM
English Words by NORMAN GIMBEL
Original Words by VINICIUS DE MORAES

G7
a samba that swings so cool and sways so gentle, that when
Gm7
G♭7
Fmaj7
she passes, each one she
he passes, each girl he
passes goes "a-a-h!"
G♭maj7
Oh, but I watch her so
him
C♭9
F♯m7
sadly. How

D9
can I tell {her / him} I love {her? / him?}
Yes,
Gm7
Eb9
I would give my heart glad - ly,
Am7
D7b9
but each day when {she / he} walks to the sea, {she / he}
Gm7
C7b9
Fmaj7
looks straight a - head not at me.
Tall and tan and young

G7
and love - ly, the girl
hand - some, the boy
from I - pa - ne - ma goes walk - ing, and when
Gm7
G♭7
Fmaj7
she
he
pass - es I smile,
but
she
he
does - n't see.
1
G♭7
2
G♭7
Fmaj7
She
He
just does - n't see.
G♭7
Fmaj7
G♭7
Fmaj7
No,
She
He
does - n't see.
rit.

GOD BLESS' THE CHILD

from BUBBLING BROWN SUGAR

Words and Music by ARTHUR HERZOG JR.
and BILLIE HOLIDAY

Bbmaj7 Bb7 Eb6 Bbmaj7 Bb7 Eb6 Fm7 Bdim7/F Bb7
strong gets more, While the weak ones fade, Emp - ty pock - ets don't ev - er
mf–p
mf
Fm7 B9b5 Bb9 Ebmaj7 Eb7 Ebm(maj7) Ebm6 Dm7 G9 G7b9
make the grade; Ma-ma may have, Pa - pa may have, But God bless the child that's
p
Cm9 F7 Bb6 Eb9 D7 Gm Gm(maj7)
got his own! That's got his own. Mon - ey, you got
p
mp
mf
Gm7 Gm6 Dm A7 D7 Gm Gm(maj7)
lots o' friends,_ Crowd - in' 'round the door, When you're gone and

Gm7 G6 Dm G7 F9♭5 F9 Cm7 F
spend - in' ends, They don't come no more. Rich re -
p
Bb♭maj7 Bb♭7 Eb♭6 Bb♭maj7 Bb♭7 Eb♭6 Fm7 Bdim7/F Bb♭7 Fm7 B9♭5 Bb♭9
la - tions give, Crust of bread, and such, You can help your - self, But don't take too much!
mf
Eb♭maj7 Eb♭6 Eb♭m(maj7) Eb♭m6 Dm7 G9 G7♭9 Cm9 F7
Ma-ma may have, Pa - pa may have, But God bless the child that's got his own! That's
p
1
Bb♭6 Gm7 C9 F♯7/C♯ Cm7 F
got his own. Them that's
3
2
Bb♭6 F♯6 Bb♭6
got his own.
R.H.

HERE'S THAT RAINY DAY

from CARNIVAL IN FLANDERS

Words by JOHNNY BURKE
Music by JIMMY VAN HEUSEN

B♭ B♭+ B♭6 B♭dim7 Am F/A

told me a - bout, and I laughed at the thought that it

D9 (4fr) Gmaj9 G6

might turn out this way.

G Gmaj7 B♭/F Em7♭5 E♭maj7 (3fr) E♭6 E♭m (6fr) E♭dim7

Where is that worn - out wish that I threw a - side,

Am7 D7 D7♭9 (4fr) Gmaj7 G6

af - ter it brought my lov - er near?

G+
Cmaj7
C7
D7/C
Fun - ny how love be - comes a
G/B
B
Gm6/B♭
A7
Am7/D
cold rain - y day. Fun - ny that
D7
1
G6
Em7
Am7
D9
D7♭9
rain - y day is here.
2
G
B♭/F
E♭maj7
Am7/D
G
here.
rall.

HAVE YOU MET MISS JONES?

from I'D RATHER BE RIGHT

Words by LORENZ HART
Music by RICHARD RODGERS

D♭7
G♭
A9
D
breath, and all at once was scared to death, and all at once I owned the
A♭m7
D♭7
G♭
C7
F
earth and sky!
Now I've met Miss
mp
F♯dim7
Gm7
C
Gm7
C7
F/A
A♭dim7
Jones, and we'll keep on meet - ing till we die,
Gm7
Gm7/C
C7
F
B♭7
F
Miss Jones and I.
rall.

HEART AND SOUL

from the Paramount Short Subject A SONG IS BORN

Words by FRANK LOESSER
Music by HOAGY CARMICHAEL

Moderately, lightly rhythmical
F
Dm7
Gm7
C7
F
Dm7
mp
Heart and soul, I fell in love with you. Heart and soul,
Gm7
C7
F
Dm
Gm
3fr
C7
mf
the way a fool would do, mad - ly, be - cause you held me
F
Dm7
Gm7
C7
F
Dm7
tight and stole a kiss in the night. Heart and soul,
Gm7
C7
F
Dm7
Gm7
C7
I begged to be a - dored. Lost con - trol and tum - bled o - ver - board

F Dm Gm 3fr C7 F Dm7
glad - ly that mag - ic night we kissed there in the
F F7 B♭ A7 D7 G7
moon - mist. Oh! but your lips were thrill - ing,
C7 F7 E7 A7 B♭ A7
much too thrill - ing. Nev - er be - fore were
D7 G7 C7 F7 E7 C7
mine so strange - ly will - ing. But

F
Dm7
Gm7
C7
F
Dm7
now I see what one em - brace can do. Look at me,
Gm7
C7
F
Dm
Gm7
C7
it's got me lov - ing you mad - ly; that lit - tle kiss you
A7
D7
Gm
G9
C7
1
F
Dm7
3fr
9fr
stole held all my heart and soul.
Gm9
C9
C7♭9
2
F
Dm7
Gm9
C7♭9
F
3fr
soul.

HELLO, YOUNG LOVERS

from THE KING AND I

Lyrics by OSCAR HAMMERSTEIN II
Music by RICHARD RODGERS

A
D/F♯
Fdim7
will. There are new lov - ers now on the
mf
mp
A7/E
E♭7♭5
D
Dm6
same si - lent hill, look - ing on the same blue sea. And I
A
Dm
know Tom and I are a part of them all, and they're all a part of Tom
G7
Gracefully
C
C6
Cmaj7
C6
and me. Hel -
rit.
mf a tempo

C (add9)
C
Cmaj7
C6
lo, young lov - ers, who - ev - er you are, I
p
Cmaj7
C6
G7/B
Fm/C
hope your trou - bles are few.
All my good
G7/B
E♭/B♭
6fr
G7/B
Dm7
Dm7/G
G7
wish - es go with you to - night—
I've been in love like
C
C (add9)
C
Cmaj7
you.
Be brave, young lov - ers, and fol - low your
mf
p

C6
Cmaj7
C6
G7/B
star, be brave and faith - ful and true.
Fm/C
G7/B
E♭/B♭
6fr
G7/B
Dm7
Cling ver - y close to each oth - er to - night—
I've been in
Dm7/G
G7
C
F/A
C7sus/G
3fr
love like you.
I know how it feels to have
mf
mp
F/A
C7sus/G
3fr
F/A
C7sus/G
3fr
C7
F
wings on your heels, and to fly down a street in a trance.

E7
Am
You fly down a street on a chance that you'll meet, and you
Dm7
Dm7/G
G7
meet — not real - ly by chance.
Don't
p
C (add9)
C
Cmaj7
C6
Cmaj7
cry, young lov - ers, what - ev - er you do, don't cry be -
C6
G7/B
Fm/C
G7/B
cause I'm a - lone.
All of my mem - 'ries are

E♭/B♭
6fr
G7/B
Dm7
G7
hap - py to - night—
I've had a love of my
C7
F/A
Fm/A♭
own,
I've had a love of my
mf
C+/G
C6/G
Dm
E♭/G
3fr
G7
own, like yours,
I've had a love of my
cresc. ed allargando
1
C6
G7
2
C6
own.
Hel -
own.
mf a tempo
p
f

HONEYSUCKLE ROSE

from AIN'T MISBEHAVIN'
from TIN PAN ALLEY

Words by ANDY RAZAF
Music by THOMAS "FATS" WALLER

Gm7 C13 Gm7 C13 G9♯5 C6 G9♯5 C13
flow - ers droop and sigh, and I know the rea - son why; you're much sweet - er,
F Gm7 F/A Fm/A♭ G7 C13 F F/C Ddim7 C7/E F F/C Cm/E♭ C(♭♭5)/E
good - ness knows, Hon - ey - suck - le Rose.
3fr
F7 Cm7/F Fdim7 F7 B♭6 F9
8fr
Don't buy sug - ar, you just have to
G♭9 F9 B♭6 G7 Dm7/G Gdim7 G7
touch my cup. You're my sug - ar;

C7 Gm7 A♭9 G9 C7 Gm7 C13
it's sweet when you stir it up. When I'm tak - in' sips
Gm7 C13 Gm7 C13 G9♯5 C6 G9♯5 C13
from your tast - ty lips, seems the hon - ey fair - ly drips; you're con - fec - tion,
F Gm7 F/A Fm/A♭ G7 C13
good - ness knows, Hon - ey - suck - le
1
F F7 B♭6 D♭7
Rose.
F A♭dim7 B♭/D
2
F F7 Fdim7 B♭m F
Rose.

I GET ALONG WITHOUT YOU VERY WELL
(Except Sometimes)

Words and Music by HOAGY CARMICHAEL
Inspired by a poem written by J.B. THOMPSON

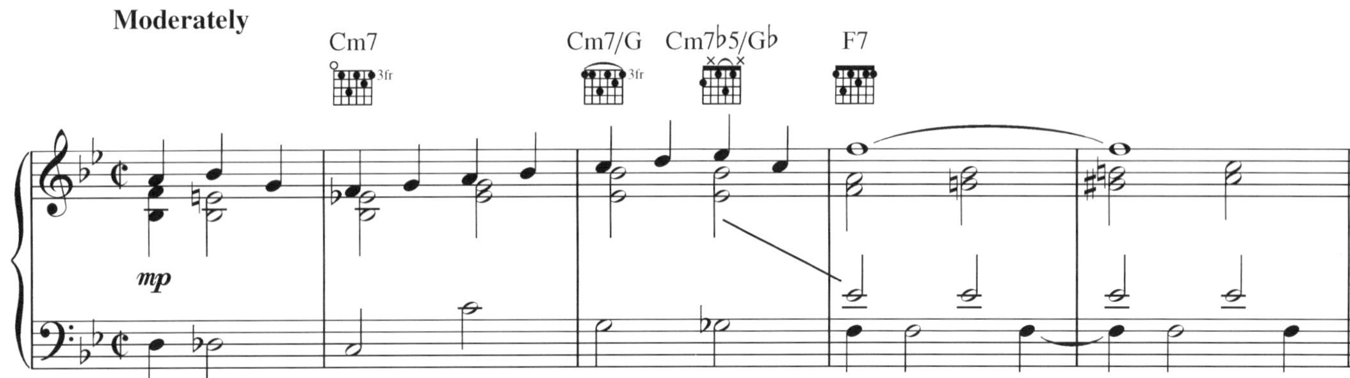

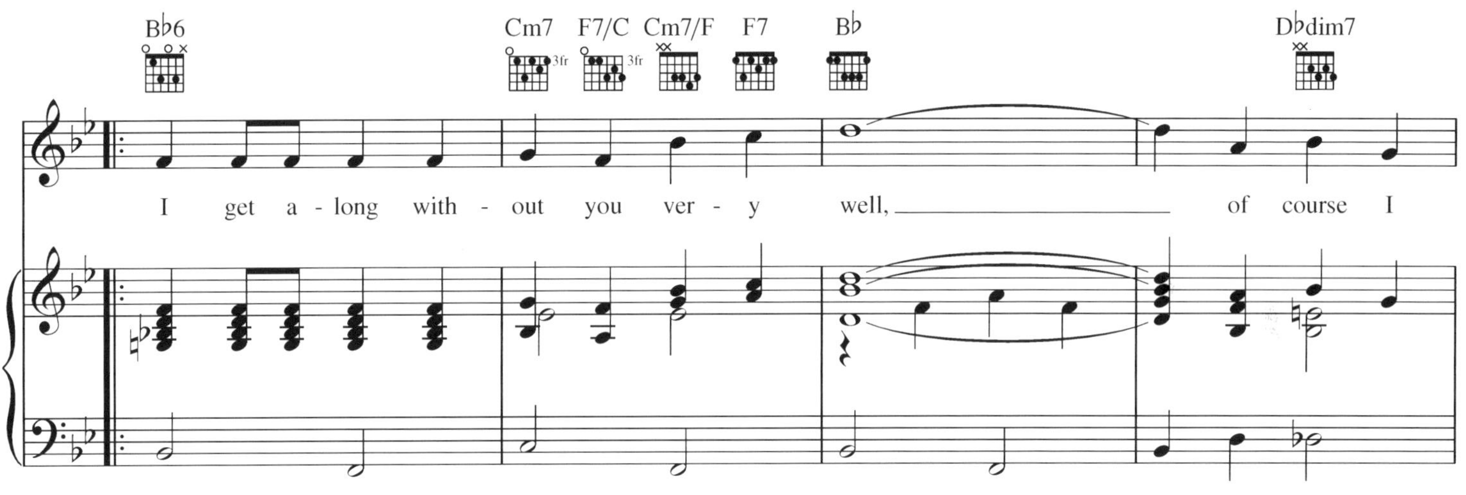

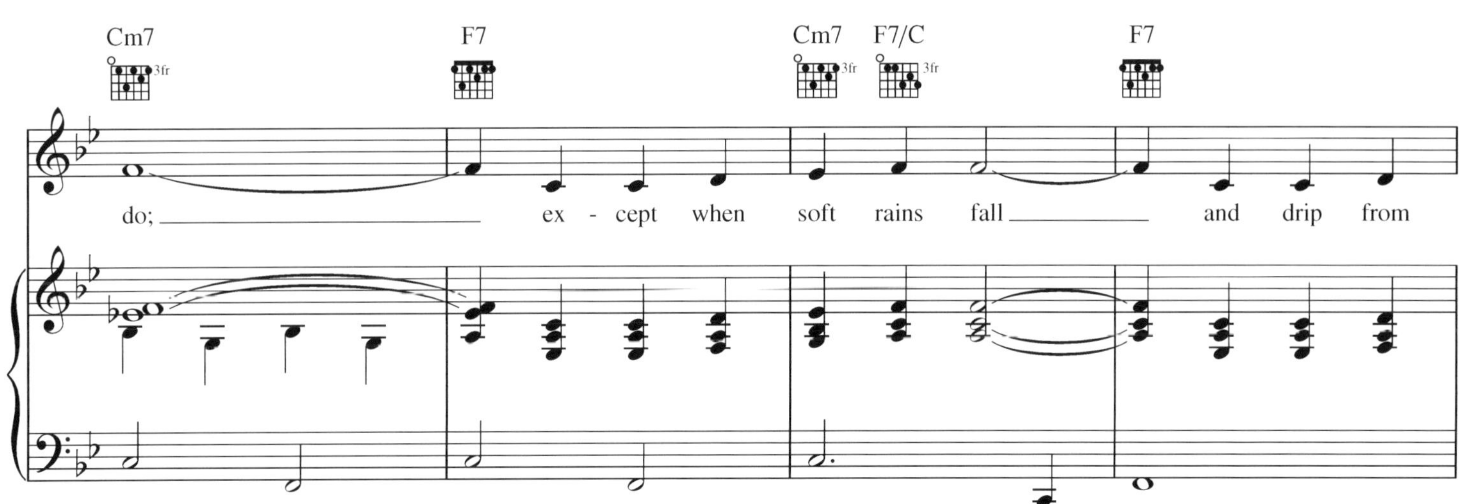

Cm7 F7/C Cm7 F7 Cm7 E♭m6
leaves, then I re - call the thrill of be - ing shel - tered in your
B♭ D♭dim7 Cm7 F7
arms, of course I do. But I
Cm7 E♭m/F B♭ Gm7
get a - long with - out you ver - y well.
Cm7 F7 B♭6 Cm7 F7/C Cm7/F F7
I've for - got - ten you, just like I

B♭
D♭dim7
Cm7
should, of course I have;
F7
Cm7
F7/C
F7
except to hear your name or someone's
Cm7
F7/C
Cm7
F7
laugh that is the same. But I've forgotten
B♭
E♭/B♭
B♭
B♭7
E♭6
you just like I should, what a guy!

E♭m
B♭
Cm
3fr
What a fool am I to think my break - ing heart
E♭m/F
F7
B♭
B♭maj7
B♭7
could kid the moon.
What's in
E♭6
D7
Gm
3fr
store?
Should I 'phone once more?
No, it's
C7
Cm/F
3fr
F7
3
best that I stick to my tune.
3

B♭6
Cm7
F7/C
Cm7/F
F7
B♭
D♭dim7
I get a - long with - out you ver - y well, of course I
Cm7
F7
Cm7
F7/C
F7
do; ex - cept per - haps in spring, but I should
Cm7
F7/C
Cm7
F7
Cm7
E♭m6
nev - er think of spring for that would sure - ly break my heart in
1
B♭
D♭dim7
Cm7
F7♭9
F7
two.
2
B♭
E♭/B♭
B♭
two.
rit.

HOW INSENSITIVE
(Insensatez)

Music by ANTONIO CARLOS JOBIM
Original Words by VINICIUS DE MORAES
English Words by NORMAN GIMBEL

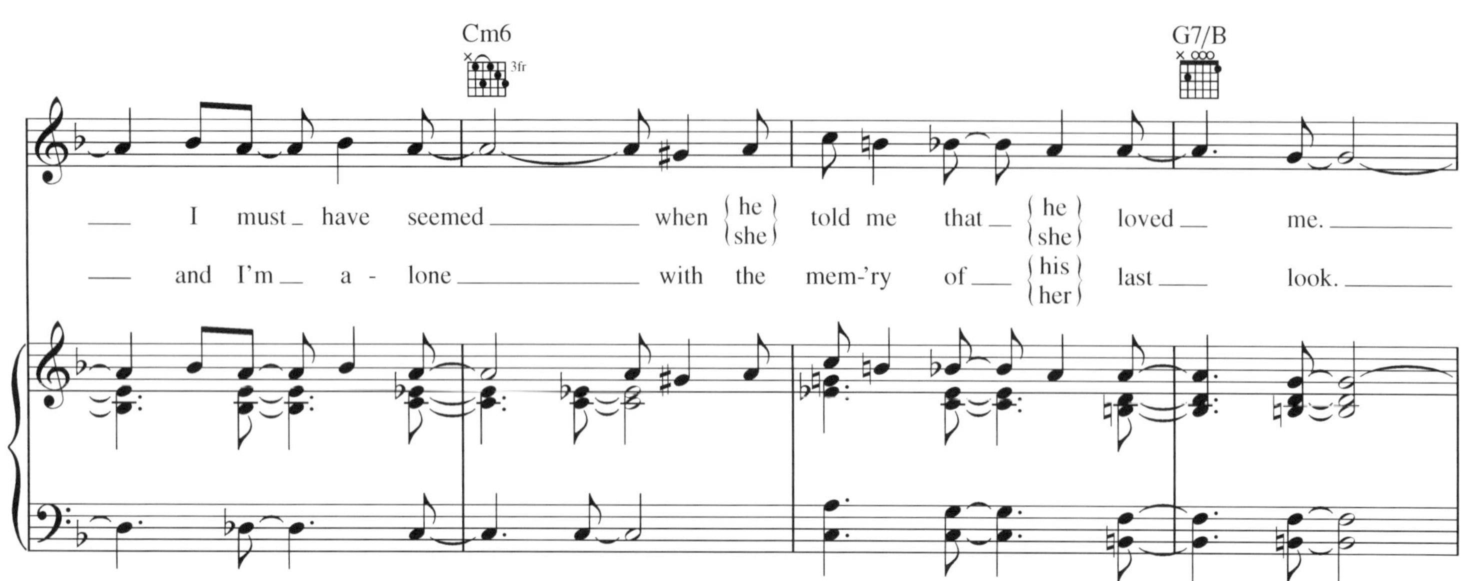

B♭6
E♭maj7
How un - moved and cold
Vague and drawn and sad,

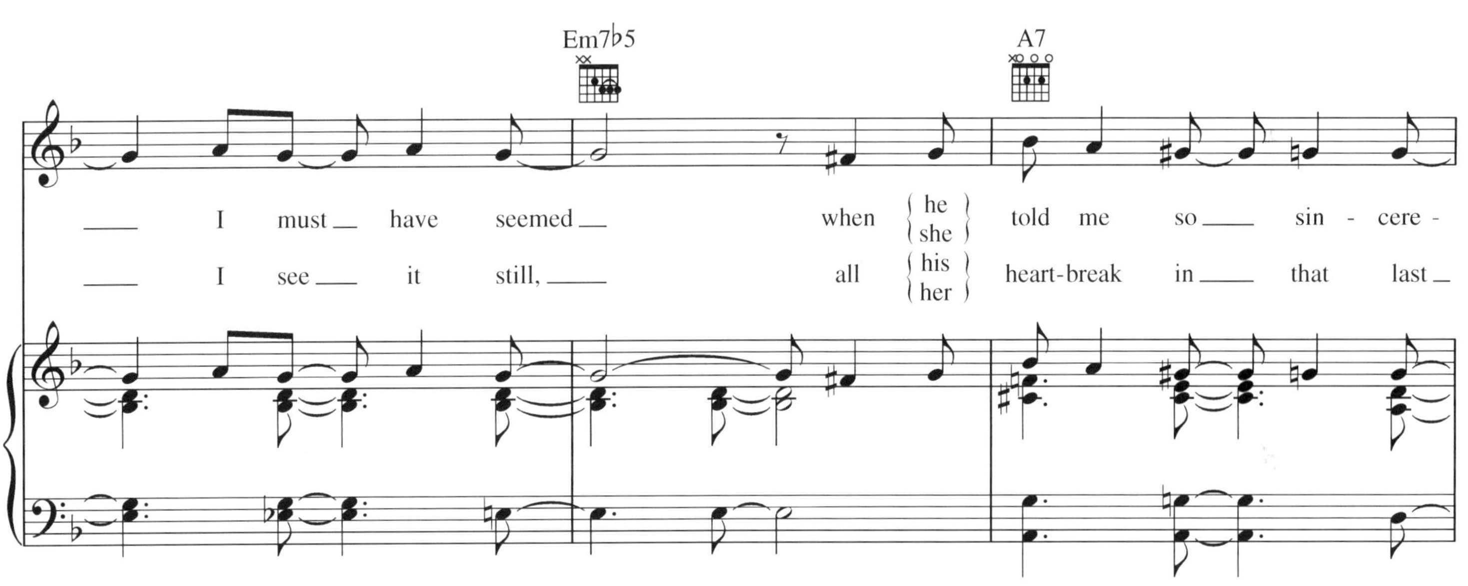
Em7♭5
A7
I must have seemed when {he / she} told me so sin - cere -
I see it still, all {his / her} heart-break in that last

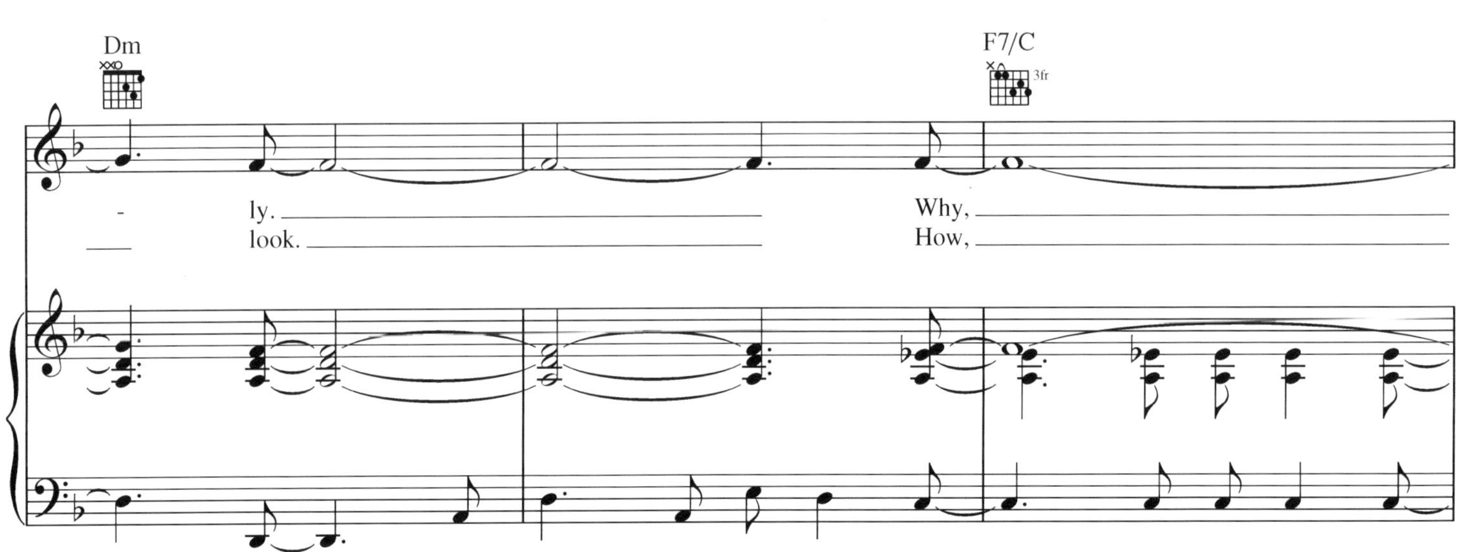
Dm
F7/C
- ly. Why,
look. How,

Bdim7
B♭maj7
he
she
must have asked,
did I just turn and
he
she
must have asked,
could I just turn and
Gm6
Dm
Cm7
stare in i - cy si - lence? What
stare in i - cy si - lence? What
F7
Bm7
E7
was I to say? What can you say
was I to do? What can one do

Portuguese Lyrics

A insensatez
Que você fez
Coração mais sem cuidado
Fez chorar de dôr
O seu amôr
Um amôr tão delicado
Ah! Porque você
Foi fraco assim
Assim tão desalmado
Ah! Meu coração
Que nunca amou
Não merece ser amado
Vai meu coração
Ouve a razão
Usa só sinceridade
Quem semeia vento
Diz a razão
Colhe tempestade
Vai meu coração
Pede perdão
Perdão apaixonado
Vai porque
Quem não
Pede perdão
Não é nunca perdoado.

I CAN'T GIVE YOU ANYTHING BUT LOVE

from BLACKBIRDS OF 1928

By JIMMY McHUGH
and DOROTHY FIELDS

D7sus D7 G G7 Bm F♯7
rot - ten to some-thing worse. Who knows, some-day I will
mate, dear, will not for - get. You have a life - time be -
Bm Bm7 E9 E7/B B♭dim7 Am7 D7
win, too. I'll be - gin to reach my prime.
fore you. I'll a - dore you, come what may.
G Cm/G C6/G Cm/G Gmaj7 G6 A9
Now, though I see what our end is, all I can spend is just my
Please don't be blue for the pres - ent, when it's so pleas - ant to hear you
C/D D7 G G/B B♭dim7 Am7
time.
say:
I can't give you an - y - thing but love,

D7
C/D
D7
G
G/B
A7
Am7/D
ba - by. That's the on - ly thing I've plen - ty of,
D7
C/D
D7
G7
C
ba - by. Dream a-while, scheme a-while; we're sure to find
A7
Am7/D
happ - pi - ness and I guess all those things you've
B♭7
A♭7
4fr
C7
D7
G
G/B
B♭dim7
al - ways pined for. Gee, I'd like to see you look - ing

Am7
D7
C/D
D7
G7
swell, ba - by; dia - mond brace - lets Wool - worth does - n't
C
A7/E
E♭7
sell, ba - by. Till that luck - y day, you know darned
G/D
E7
Am7
Em6/D
C/D
D7
well, ba - by, I can't give you an - y - thing but
1
G
B♭dim7
Am7
D7
love.
2
G
Am7♭5
G
love.

I COULD WRITE A BOOK

from PAL JOEY

Words by LORENZ HART
Music by RICHARD RODGERS

Gm7
C7
Fmaj7
Em7
A7
But my bus - y mind is burn - ing to use what learn - ing I've got.
D7
G/D
G7
Dm7
G7
I won't waste an - y time; I'll strike while the i - ron is hot. If they
C
G7
C
G7
asked me, I could write a book a - bout the
C
G7
C6
C♯dim7
Dm7
G7
G7/F
way you walk and whis - per and look. I could

C/E
A♭7/E♭
Dm7
G7
C
Cdim7
write a pre - face on how we
G/B
C
Cdim7
G/B
E♭7/B♭
6fr
Am7
D7
met so the world would nev - er for -
G
Dm7
G7
C
get. And the sim - ple
G7
C
G7
se - cret of the plot is just to

C G7 C6 C♯dim7 Dm7
tell them that I love you a lot.
G7 G7/F C/E A♭7/E♭ Dm7 G7
Then the world dis - cov - ers, as
Gm7 C7 F Dm7 C/G C+/E F6 G7
my book ends, how to make two lov - ers of
1 C Dm7 G7
friends. If they
2 C F F/C C
friends.

I DIDN'T KNOW WHAT TIME IT WAS

from TOO MANY GIRLS

Words by LORENZ HART
Music by RICHARD RODGERS

E7 A7♭5/E♭ D9 Am7/G G/D Am7/G G/D
And now I know I was na - ïve!
Slowly and tenderly
F♯m7 B7 Bm7/E Em F♯m7 B7
I did - n't know what time it was, Then I met
A Am Em Bm
you. Oh, what a love - ly time it was,
C Bm Am Dm7 D7 F♯m7 B7
How sub - lime it was, too! I did - n't

Em F♯m7 B7 A Am
know what day it was. You held my hand, Warm like the
Em Bm C Bm Am7 Dm7 D7
month of May it was, And I'll say it was grand.
G Am B7 Am B7
Grand to be a - live, to be young, to be mad, to be yours a -
mf più espressivo
Em C D7 Gmaj7
lone! Grand to see your face, feel your touch, hear your

Em7
A7
Am7
Dm7
D7
F♯m7
B7
Em
voice say I'm all your own!
I didn't know what year it was,
p
F♯m7
B7
A
Am
Em
Bm
Life was no prize.
I want - ed love and here it was
C
Bm
Am7
Cm
3fr
G
B7
C6
D7
C6
Shin - ing out of your eyes.
I'm wise and I know what time it is
1
G
C♯m7♭5
4fr
D7
2
G
G6
now!
now!
mf
f
8vb

I HEAR A RHAPSODY

By GEORGE FRAJOS,
JACK BAKER and DICK GASPARRE

Cm
Ab
Bb7#5
Eb
spark - ling eyes are smil - ing at me,
Edim
Fm
Abm6
Bb7
Gm
Bb7
then soft through the star - lit skies I hear a
Abm6
Eb
Cm6
D7sus
D7
Gm
rhap - so - dy. My days are so
Ebdim
Gm
Bb+
blue when you're a - way.

B♭
Fm
Fm6
G7♭9
G7
My heart looks for you, so won't you stay?
G
F♯dim
G7
Cm
A♭
B♭7♯5
My dar - ling, hold me tight and
E♭
Edim
Fm
A♭m6
whis - per to me. Then soft through a star - ry night
B♭7
Gm
B♭7
A♭m6
E♭
F♯dim
G7
E♭6
optional 2nd time
I hear a rhap - so - dy. And when I
rall. e dim.
p

I SHOULD CARE

Words and Music by SAMMY CAHN,
PAUL WESTON and AXEL STORDAHL

E7sus
E7
C7
Fmaj7
sleep well 'cept for a dream or two,
Bm7♭5
E7♭9
Am
D7
but, then, I count my sheep well. Fun - ny how sheep can
F/G
Dm7
G(add6)
Dm7
G7
Cmaj7
lull you to sleep. So, I should care,
Dm7
F/G
Cmaj7
Em7♭5
I should let it up - set me. I should

A7sus A7 Dm7 Dm7♭5
care but it just does - n't get me.
Am A7♯5 A7 Dm7 E7 Am(maj7) Am/G D7 E♭m7
May - be I won't find some - one as love - ly as you, but,
Dm7 G7 1C Am7 Dm7 Fm7 F Em7
I should care and I do.
2C Fmaj7 D♭ Cmaj7
do.
rit.

I HEAR MUSIC

from the Paramount Picture DANCING ON A DIME

Words by FRANK LOESSER
Music by BURTON LANE

F♯m7♭5 F7 E7 Am Am7/G F♯m7♭5 F7 E7
Pol - ly - an - na, shout - in' out a loud ho - san - na.
Am Am7/G F♯m7♭5 G7 C7
It's my sing - ing heart I can't con - trol.
Am7♭5 D7♯5 G7 C7 Am7♭5 D7♯5 G7 C7
I hear mu - sic, might - y fine mu - sic, the
F7 B♭ F7 B♭ C7 F
mur - mur of a morn - ing breeze up there, the rat - tle of the milk - man

C7 F Am7♭5 D7♯5 G7 C7 Am7♭5 D7♯5
on the stair. Sure that's mu - sic, might - y fine
G7 C7 F7 B♭ F7 B♭
mu - sic, the sing - ing of a spar - row in the sky, the
C7 F C7 F Cm7 F9 Cm7 F9
3fr
perk - ing of the cof - fee right near - by. There's my fa - v'rite
B♭maj7 B♭6 B♭maj7 B♭6 B♭m7 E♭9 B♭m7 E♭7
mel - o - dy, you, my an - gel,

A♭ Gm7 C7 Am7♭5 D7♯5 G7 C7
phon - ing me. I hear mu - sic,
Am7♭5 D7♯5 G7 C7 F7 B♭
might - y fine mu - sic, and an - y - time I think my
F7 B♭ C7 F Gm7 Gm7/C C7
world is wrong, I get me out of bed and sing this
1 F Gm7 C7
song.
2 F Gm7 G♭9 Fmaj7
song.

I REMEMBER YOU

from the Paramount Picture THE FLEET'S IN

Words by JOHNNY MERCER
Music by VICTOR SCHERTZINGER

G
Gdim
G
I re - mem - ber you.
You're the one who
F
G7sus
G7
Cmaj7
C6
Cm
D7♭9
made my dreams come true a few kiss - es a -
G
D7sus
D7
G
Gdim
go.
I re - mem - ber you.
G
F
G7sus
G7
Cmaj7
C6
You're the one who said: "I love you, too." I

Cm
D7♭9
G
Dm7/G
G9
do. Did - n't you know?
C
F♯m7
B7
E
I re - mem - ber too a dis - tant bell
F♯m7
B7
Emaj7
E6
Em7
A7
and stars that fell like rain, out of the
Dmaj7
D6
D7
G
blue. When my life is

Gdim
G
Bm7♭5
E7♭9
through and the an - gels ask me to re -
Am
Cm
3fr
Cm6
3fr
G
call the thrill of them all,
A9
5fr
G
G/B
B♭dim7
Am7
D7♭9
4fr
then I shall tell them I re - mem - ber
1
G
A9/G
5fr
D7
you.
2
G
A7♭9
5fr
D13
4fr
G
you.

I THOUGHT ABOUT YOU

Words by JOHNNY MERCER
Music by JIMMY VAN HEUSEN

Fm7
Bb13
5 fr
Eb
3 fr
D7
What did I find?
I took a trip on the train
Db9b5
C9
F9
Cm7
3 fr
F7
and I thought a-bout you.
Fm7
Bb
G7
Cm
3 fr
I passed a shad-ow-y lane
and I thought a-bout you.
Bbm7
Eb13
5 fr
Ab
4 fr
Abm6
4 fr
Two or three cars parked un-der the stars, a

Eb/Bb
Bb/Ab
Gm7
Cm7
D7sus
D7
wind - ing stream, moon shin-ing down on
D7sus
D7
Gm
Edim7
Fm7
Bb7
some lit-tle town, and with each beam, same old dream.
Eb
D7
Db9b5
C9
F9
At ev - 'ry stop that me made, oh, I thought a-bout you.
Cm7
F7
Fm7
Bb
G7
But when I pulled down the shade, then I

Cm
Bbm7
Eb7
Ab
Ab6
real - ly felt blue.
I peeked thru the crack _ and
Abm6
Eb
Eb6
Ab9
F9
F#dim7
looked at the track, _ the one go-ing back _ to you. And
Fm7
Bb13
Fm7
Bb7b9
1
Eb6
Cm
what did I do? _ I thought a-bout you!
Fm7
Fm9/Bb
Bb7
2
Eb6
E7#9
Eb6

I'LL BE AROUND

Words and Music by
ALEC WILDER

A♭maj9
A♭6
Fm7
G7
C
Dm7
C/E
F
Your lat - est love can nev - er
G6
G♯dim7
F/A
G7/B
C
Am
Dm7
G13
G13♭9
last, and when it's past, I'll be a - round when he's she's
C
Dm7
F
C/E
Dm7
C
D♭7/A♭
Gm7
B♭/C
gone. Good - bye a - gain, and
D♭7/A♭
Gm7
B♭/C
C7♭9
Fmaj7
F6
A♭7/E♭
Dm7
if you find a love like mine, just now and

G13 G13♭9 C/E Am Dm7 G13♭9

then drop a line to say you're feel - ing fine. And

C Dm7 C/E F G6 G♯dim7

when things go wrong, per - haps you'll see you're meant for

Dm/A G7/B C Am Dm7 G13 G13♭9

me, so I'll be a - round when {he's / she's}

1

C E♭9 A♭maj9 A♭6 Fm7 G7

gone.

2

C Dm7 F C/E Dm7 C

gone.

I'LL NEVER SMILE AGAIN

Words and Music by
RUTH LOWE

E♭dim7
Fm7
B7
B♭7
E♭
D♭
D
I'll never laugh again, what good would it do?
E♭
B7♯5
B♭7
E♭
A♭m/C♭
B♭7♯5
For tears would fill my eyes, my heart would realize
E♭maj7
D9
G
D7/A
G/B
F♯dim7
Fm7
that our romance is through.
B♭7
E♭
E♭dim7
Fm7
B7
B♭7
E♭
I'll never love again; I'm so in love with you.
a tempo

E♭dim7 Fm7 B7 B♭7
3
I'll nev - er thrill a - gain to some - bod - y
3
E♭7 A♭maj7 A♭6 A♭m/C♭
3fr
4fr
new. With - in my heart I
E♭ Gm7 C7 Fm7 B7♯5 B♭7
3fr
3
know I will nev - er start to smile a - gain un - til I smile at
1
E♭ E♭dim7 B♭7 E♭ E♭dim7
3fr
3fr
you. I'll nev - er
2
E♭ B7/E E♭6
3fr
you.

I'LL REMEMBER APRIL

Words and Music by PAT JOHNSON,
DON RAYE and GENE DE PAUL

Am7
D7♭9
4fr
Gmaj9
G6
mem - ber A - pril and be glad. I'll
Cm7
3fr
F7
B♭maj7
B♭6
be con - tent you loved me once in A - pril. Your
Cm7
3fr
F7
B♭maj7
lips were warm and love and spring were new.
B♭6
Am7
D7
3
But I'm not a - fraid of au - tumn and her

Gmaj9 G6 F♯m7 B9
sor - row, for I'll re - mem - ber A - pril and
Emaj7 E6 Am7 D7 G G6
you. The fire will dwin - dle in - to
Gmaj7 G6 Gm7 Gm6
glow - ing ash - es, for flames and love live such a
Gm7 Gm6 Am7♭5
lit - tle while. I won't for - get,

D7
F9
E9
E7
but I won't be lone - ly
I'll re -
Am7
D7♭9
4fr
1
G
mem - ber A - pril
and I'll smile.
G6
Gmaj7
G6
2
G
smile.
G6
G
G6/9
decresc.

I'LL TAKE ROMANCE

Lyrics by OSCAR HAMMERSTEIN II
Music by BEN OAKLAND

2
F6
Gm7
C7♭9
F
E♭m7
mance.
So, my
lov - er, when you
want
A♭7
D♭dim
D♭6
E♭m7
me,
call
me
in the
A♭7
D♭dim
D♭6
G♭7
hush of the eve - ning.
When
you
C♭maj7
A♭m6
F
G♭dim7
call
me,
in the
hush of the

C7
F
Dm7
Gm7
C7
evening, I'll rush to my first real ro - mance. While my
F
A♭7
D♭maj7
Gm7♭5
C7sus
G♭dim7
heart is young and eager and gay, I'll give my heart a -
Gm7
C7
F
Dm7
Gm7
way. I'll take ro - mance.
Fdim7
F
I'll take my own ro - mance.

I'M BEGINNING TO SEE THE LIGHT

Words and Music by DON GEORGE, JOHNNY HODGES,
DUKE ELLINGTON and HARRY JAMES

G6 E♭7 D7 G6 E♭7 D7

nev - er went in for af - ter - glow or can - dle - light on the

E♭7 G6 Em D7 G Dm6/F E7

mis - tle - toe, but now when you turn the lamp down low, I'm be -

A7 Am7 D7 G B7

gin - ning to see the light. Used to ram - ble

B♭7

through the park, shad - ow - box - ing in the dark.

A7
Eb7
Then you came and caused a spark that's a four a-larm fire now.
Am7
D7
G6
Eb7
D7
G6
I nev-er made love by lan-tern shine, I
Eb7
D7
Eb7
G6
Em
D7
nev-er saw rain-bows in my wine, but now that your lips are
G
Dm6/F
E7
A7
Am7
D7
1 G Gm7b5
D9
2 G D7#5(b9)
G6
burn-ing mine, I'm be-gin-ning to see the light. I
8vb

I'M OLD FASHIONED

from YOU WERE NEVER LOVELIER

Words by JOHNNY MERCER
Music by JEROME KERN

F F6 Dm7 C/G C6/G Am
not that I ev - er try to be a saint,
Fmaj7 E7 E7♯5 B7 G7 C Cmaj7 Dm7/A G7/B
I'm the type that they class - i - fy as quaint.
rall.
a tempo
C C7/B♭ F6/A C7/G F Gm7 C7
5fr
I'm old fash - ioned, I
rall.
a tempo
F C6 F Am7 F/A
love the moon - light, I love the old fash - ioned

Em7♭5
A7
Dm7
G7
things; the sound of rain up -
Dm7
D7
Gm
3fr
G7/B
on a win - dow - pane, the star - ry song that A - pril
C7sus
C7
F6
Gm7
C7
sings. This year's fan - cies are
Fmaj7
Bm7
E7
A
E7/B
A/C♯
D7
pass - ing fan - cies, but sigh - ing sighs, hold - ing hands,

E7
F#dim7
Gm7
C7
F
Gm7
C7
these my heart un - der - stands. I'm old fash - ioned, but
F
C6
C/B♭
Am7
F/A
B♭maj7
B♭dim7
I don't mind it, that's how I want to be, as
Am7
F6/A
G7
F/C
Gm7
C7
long as you a - gree to stay, old fash - ioned with
rall. e dim.
1
F
Fmaj7
Gm7
C7
2
F
F6
me.
me.
a tempo
rit.

IF I WERE A BELL

from GUYS AND DOLLS

By FRANK LOESSER

F F/E♭ B♭/D B♭m/D♭ C7♭9 F F/E♭ B♭/D B♭m/D♭ C7♭9
mo - ment we kissed to - night that's the way I've just got to be - have. Boy, if
knew my mo - rale would crack from the won - der - ful way that you looked. Boy, if
F6 B♭9 A B♭7 A
I were a lamp I'd light, Or if I were a ban - ner I'd wave.
I were a duck I'd quack, Or if I were a goose I'd be cooked.
A7/E E♭dim G9 C13 C13♭9
6fr 9fr 2fr 3fr
Ask me how do I feel, lit - tle me with my qui - et up -
Ask me how do I feel, ask me now that we're fond - ly ca -
F6 C(add9)/E Fm6 F♯dim7
bring - ing. Well, sir, all I can say is if I
ress - ing. Pal, if I were a sal - ad I know

E♭7 D7 G9 Gm7♭5/D♭ C7 C7♭9
___ were a gate ___ I'd be swing - ing. ___ And if
___ I'd be splash - ing my dress - ing. ___ Or if
F F/E♭ B♭/D A♭dim7 F/A E7♯5
I were a watch I'd start pop - ping my spring, ___
I were a sea - son I'd sure - ly be spring, ___
E♭7 D9 D7♭9 Dm7/G G9♭5 Fmaj7 Dm7 B♭maj7 C9
___ Or if I were a bell ___ I'd go ding dong ding dong
___ Or if I were a bell ___ I'd go ding dong ding dong
1 F6/9 A♭dim Gm9 A7/E E♭dim
ding. Ask me
2 F6/9 E♭6/9 F6/9
ding. ___
ff

IN A SENTIMENTAL MOOD

Words and Music by DUKE ELLINGTON, IRVING MILLS and MANNY KURTZ

Dm
Dm(maj7)
Dm7
Dm6
Gm
Gm(maj7)
3fr
kiss drifts a mel - o - dy so strange and sweet.
Gm7
C9
Dm
D9
4fr
C♯dim/D
3fr
Ddim
D7
In this sen - ti - men - tal bliss you make my par - a -
Gm7
G♭7♭5
G♭7
F6
A♭13
4fr
D♭maj7
B♭m7
dise com - plete. Rose pet - als seem to fall, it's
E♭m7
6fr
G♭/A♭
A♭13
4fr
D♭
B♭9♯5
B♭13
6fr
E♭7♯5
E♭13
5fr
A♭7♯5
4fr
A♭13
4fr
all like a dream to call you mine.
3
3
3

D♭maj7 B♭m7 E♭m7 G♭/A♭ A♭13 C7
6fr
4fr
My heart's a light - er thing since you made this night a thing di - vine.
N.C.
Dm Dm(maj7) Dm7 Dm6
In a sen - ti - men - tal mood, I'm with - in a world so
Gm Gm(maj7) Gm7 C9 Dm
3fr
3fr
heav - en - ly, for I nev - er dreamt that you'd be lov - ing
D9 C♯dim/D Ddim D7 Gm7 G♭7♭5 G♭7
4fr
3fr
1
F6
N.C.
2
F6 Fmaj6/9
sen - ti - men - tal me. In a sen - ti - men - tal me.

ILL WIND
(You're Blowin' Me No Good)
from COTTON CLUB PARADE

Lyric by TED KOEHLER
Music by HAROLD ARLEN

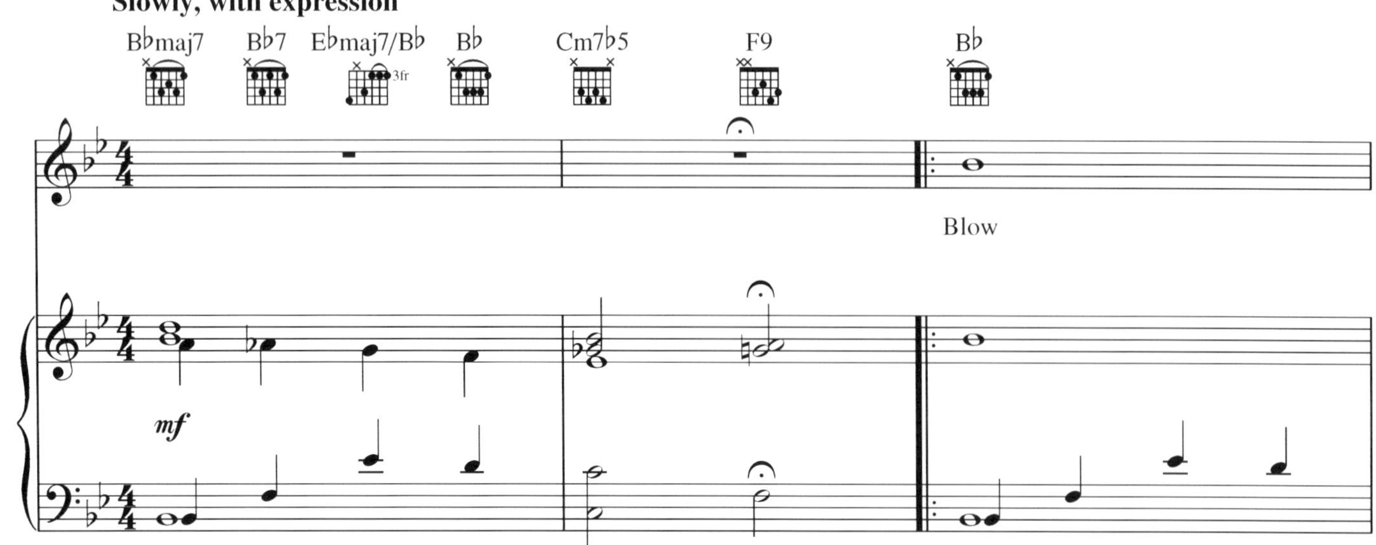

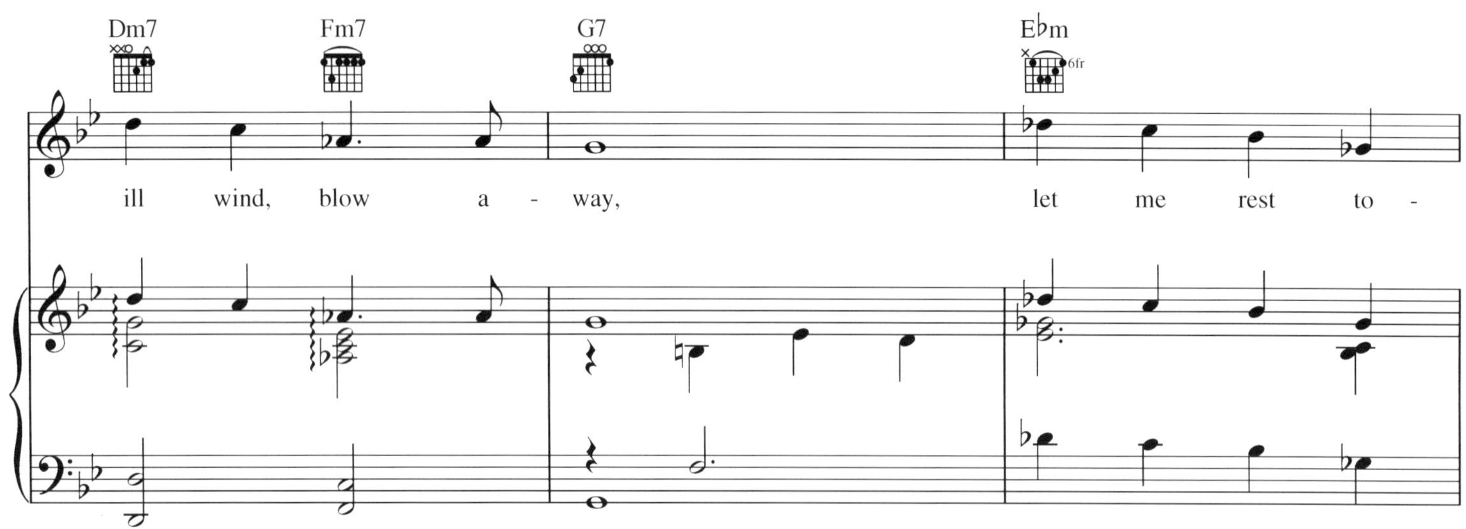

F7♯5
B♭
E♭7
F7
no
good.
B♭
Dm7
Fm7
G7
Go,
ill
wind,
go
a - way,
E♭m
6fr
B♭
F7sus
skies
are,
oh,
so
gray
a - round
my
neigh - bor -
B♭
F7♯5
B♭
hood,
and
that's
no
good.

E♭7
F7
D7
Em7
Fm
D7
You're on - ly mis - lead - in' the sun - shine I'm need - in',
G7
Edim
3fr
G7
3
ain't that a shame? It's
D7
Em7
Fm
D7
F/G
G7
so hard to keep up with trou - bles that creep up from out of no - where, when
Cm7♭5
F7♯5
F7
B♭
Dm7
Fm7
love's to blame. So ill wind, blow a -

G7
E♭m
6fr
B♭
way.
Let me rest to - day.
You're
F7sus
B♭
B♭m
A♭7
4fr
blow - in' me no good,
no
B♭
A♭
4fr
1
B♭
good,
no good.
Cm7♭5
Cm7
3fr
F7
2
B♭
good.

IN THE WEE SMALL HOURS OF THE MORNING

Words by BOB HILLIARD
Music by DAVID MANN

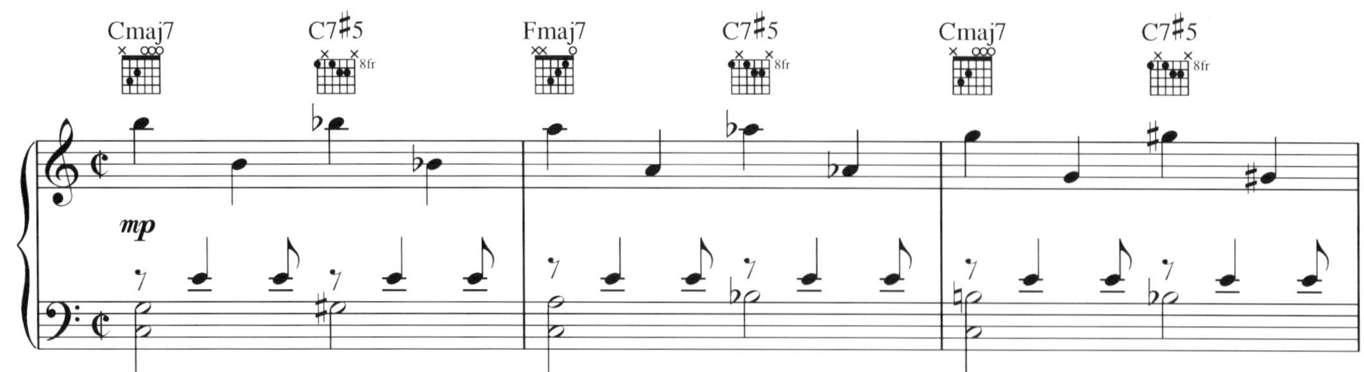

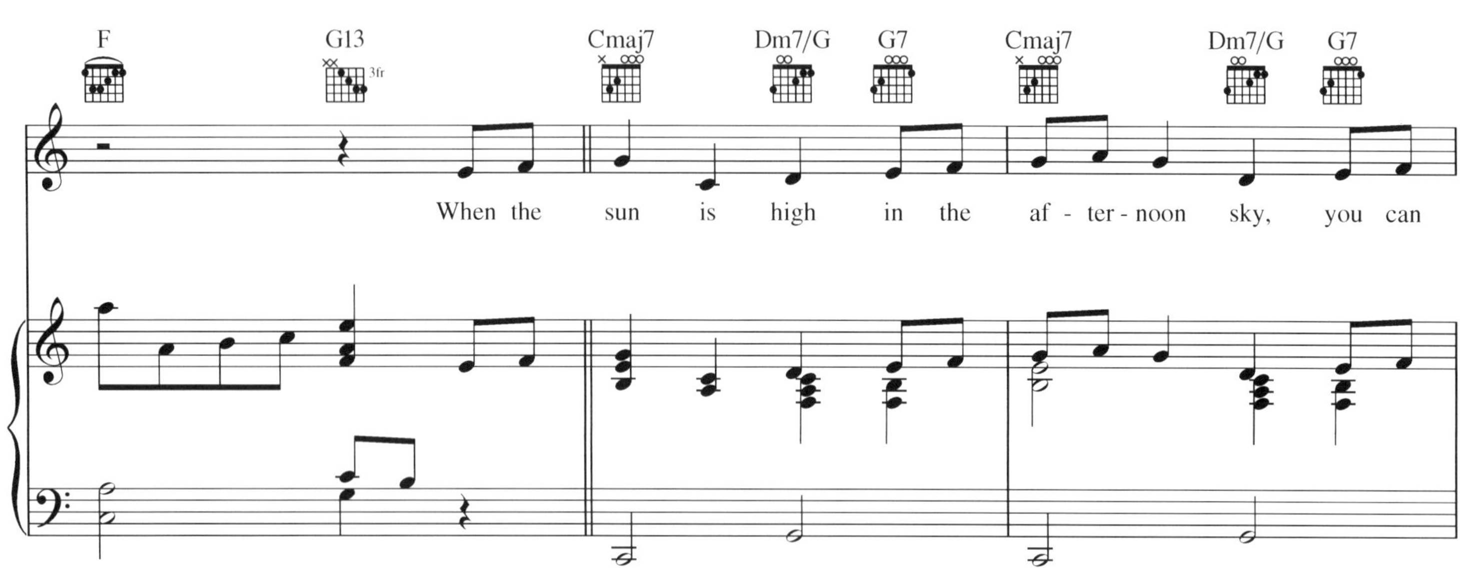

Em7
F♯m7/B
B7♭9
Em7
A7♭9
5fr
D7
G7
clock ticks on, something happens to you. In the
Cmaj7
C7
C6
C+
C
C+
wee small hours of the morn - ing, while the whole wide world is fast a -
Dm/C
G9/B
9fr
Gm/B♭
A7
sleep, you lie a - wake and think a - bout the girl, boy, and
Am6/C
B7
Em
G7
Cmaj7
C7
nev - er ev - er think of count - ing sheep. When your lone - ly heart has learned its

C6 C+ Cmaj7 Gm/B♭ A7 Dm7 D♯dim7
les - son, you'd be {hers / his} if on - ly {she / he} would call. In the wee small hours of the
C/E Gm/B♭ A7
1
Dm7 Dm7/G G7♭9 C6 G7
morn - ing that's the way you miss {her / him} most of all. In the
2
Dm7 D7 D♭7♯9 3fr C6 F Cmaj7
time you miss {her / him} most of all.

IN WALKED BUD

By THELONIOUS MONK

Fm
Db9#11
Gm7b5 C7b9 Fm(add2)
Fm(add2)/E
Fm9/Eb
Bb7/D
Eb7
Ab6
F7#9
Bbm6
Eb7
To Coda
Ab6
C7b9
Gm7b5 C7b9
Fm
Fm(maj7)
Fm7

Bb7
Eb7
Ab6
F7#9
Bbm9
Eb7#5(b9)
Abmaj9
Gm7b5
C7b9
Fm9
Fm(maj7)
Fm9
Bb13
Eb7b5
Ab6
F7#9
Bbm9
Eb7
Ab
D.S. al Coda
Gm7b5
C7b9
CODA
Ab6

INVITATION

Words by PAUL FRANCIS WEBSTER
Music by BRONISLAU KAPER

A♭7
4fr
strangers out of the blue suddenly you are
D♭7♭9
C♯m7
4fr
there. Wher-ev-er I go
F♯7♯5(♭9)
Bm
you're the glow of temp-ta-tion,
Bm7
E7♯5(♭9)
6fr
Am9
5fr
glanc-ing my way in the gray of the dawn.

Am7
D7♯5(♭9)
And al - ways your eyes smile that strange in - vi -
Gm
Gm7
E♭7♯9(♯11)
ta - tion. Then you are gone, where, oh, where have you
D7♭9
G7♯5
G7
Cm7
gone? How long must I stay in a world of il -
F7
lu - sion, be where you are, so near yet so far a -

B♭7♭9(♯11)
E♭m7
part.
Hop - ing you'll say
C♭9♭5
F7♭5
with a warm in - vi - ta - tion,
"Where have you been? Dar - ling, come
B♭7
E♭m
A♭
A♭7
G7♭5(♭9)
in, come in - to my heart."
Cm9
E♭m
heart."

IS YOU IS, OR IS YOU AIN'T
(Ma' Baby)
from FOLLOW THE BOYS
from FIVE GUYS NAMED MOE

Words and Music by BILLY AUSTIN
and LOUIS JORDAN

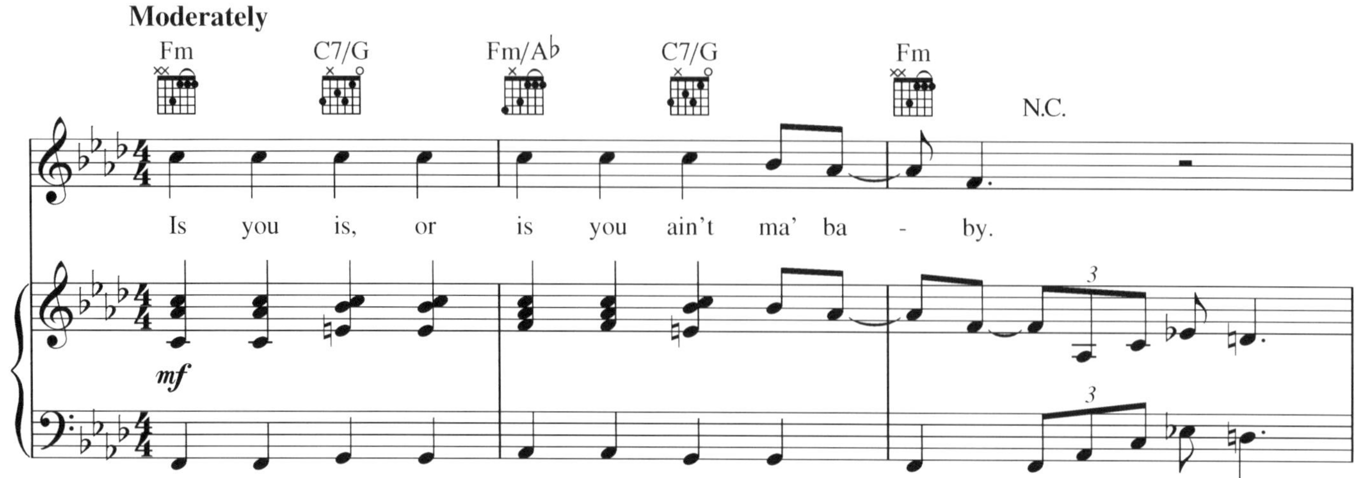

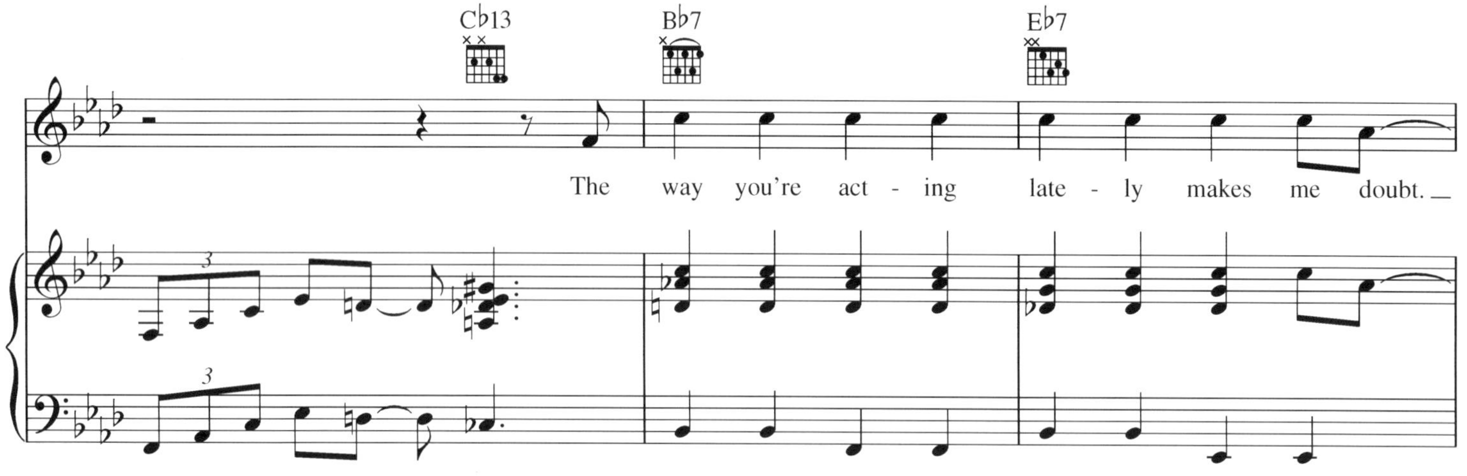

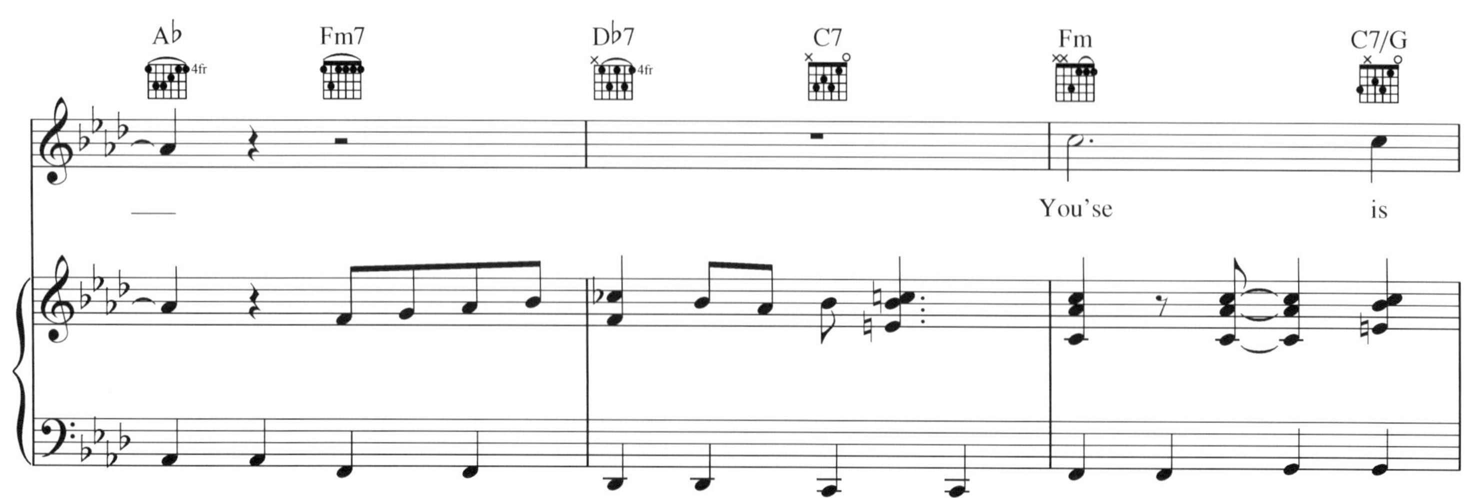

Fm/A♭ C7/G Fm N.C. C♭13
still my ba - by, ba - by.
B♭7 E♭7 A♭ Fm7 E♭7♯5 E♭7 A♭ A♭+
Seems my flame in your heart's done gone out. A
D♭ D♭m A♭ A♭7 A♭+
wom-an is
man is just
a crea-ture that has al - ways been strange. Just
D♭ D♭m G♭9 F7 B♭m Gm7♭5(♭9) C7
when you're sure of one you find
she's
he's
gone and made a change.

Fm
C7/G
Fm/A♭
C7/G
Fm
N.C.
C♭13
Is you is, or is you ain't ma' ba - by.
B♭7
E♭7
G♭9
3fr
F7
May - be ba - by's found some - bod - y new,
or
B♭7
1
E♭7
A♭
4fr
Fm7
D♭7
4fr
C7
is ma' ba - by, still ma' ba - by true?
2
E♭7
A♭
4fr
N.C.
still ma' ba - by true?

ISN'T IT ROMANTIC?

from the Paramount Picture LOVE ME TONIGHT

Words by LORENZ HART
Music by RICHARD RODGERS

Eb/G C7 Fm7 Bb7
kiss just the thing I miss on a night like
mance! I don't give a stitch if I don't get
Eb Ab Abm Eb/G Gbdim7
this. If dreams are made of i - mag - i - na - tion, I'm not a -
rich. A cus - tom tai - lor who has no cus - tom, is like a
Fm7 Bb7#5 Ebmaj7
fraid of my own cre - a - tion. With all my
sail - or, no one will trust 'em. But there is
Ab Bb7 Eb/G Adim
heart, my heart is here for you to take. Why should I
mag - ic in the mu - sic of my shears; I shed no

Steadily, not too fast
B♭7 E♭6 F7 B♭7 E♭
quake? I'm not a - wake. Is - n't it ro - man - tic?
tears. Lend me your ears! Is - n't it ro - man - tic?
B♭7 E♭ B♭7♯5 E♭ B♭7
Mu - sic in the night, a dream that can be heard. Is - n't it ro -
Soon I will have found some girl that I a - dore. Is - n't it ro -
E♭ B♭7 E♭
man - tic? Mov - ing shad - ows write the old - est mag - ic
man - tic? While I sit a - round, my love can scrub the
C7♯5 C7 Fm C7 Fm B♭7 G7
word. I hear the breez - es play - ing
floor. She'll kiss me ev - 'ry hour,
3fr
6fr
8fr

Cm G7♯5 Cm E♭7/B♭ A♭ C7/G

in the trees a - bove. While
or she'll get the sack. And

Fm B♭7 Bdim7 Cm F9 B♭dim7 B♭7

all the world is say - ing you were meant for love. Is - n't it ro -
when I take a show - er she can scrub my back. Is - n't it ro -

E♭ B♭7 E♭ B♭7♯5

man - tic? Mere - ly to be young on such a night as
man - tic? On a moon - light night she'll cook me on - ion

E♭ B♭7 E♭ B♭7

this? Is - n't it ro - man - tic? Ev - 'ry note that's sung is
soup. Kid - dies are ro - man - tic, and if we don't fight, we

E♭ C7♯5 C7 Fm C7 Fm

like a lov - er's kiss. Sweet
soon will have a troupe! We'll

B♭7 G7 Cm Cm/B♭ Cm/A A♭m6

sym - bols in the moon - light, do you mean that I will fall in
help the pop - u - la - tion, it's a du - ty that we owe to

E♭/G Edim7 B♭7 1 E♭ G♭dim7

love per - chance? Is - n't it ro - mance?
dear old France. Is - n't it ro -

B♭7 2 E♭ A♭m6 E♭6

Is - n't it ro - mance?

IT COULD HAPPEN TO YOU

from the Paramount Picture AND THE ANGELS SING

Words by JOHNNY BURKE
Music by JAMES VAN HEUSEN

C7sus/G
C7/G
Fm
B♭7
B♭7/A♭
E♭/G
look so wise, don't show your scorn;
B♭m7/A♭
Gm7♭5
A♭
Am7
D7sus
D7
watch your - self, I warn you.
G
G♯dim7
Am
A♯dim7
Hide your heart from sight, lock your dreams at night.
G/B
C
B7
Bm7♭5
E7
It could hap - pen to you.

Am7
Cm
3fr
G
F♯m7
B7
Don't count stars or you might stum - ble.
Em
C7/E
A7
Am7
Some - one drops a sigh, and down you
Am6
A♭9
4fr
G
G♯dim7
tum - ble. Keep an eye on spring,
Am
A♯dim7
G/B
run when church bells ring. It could
3

C
B7
Bm7♭5
E7
Am7
hap - pen to you.
All I
Cm
3fr
G/D
Bm7♭5
E7
did was won - der how your arms would be
Am7
D9
4fr
D7♭9
4fr
1
G
Em
and it hap - pened to me!
Am7
D7♯5(♭9)
4fr
2
G
C6
C9
G
me!

IT MIGHT AS WELL BE SPRING

from STATE FAIR

Lyrics by OSCAR HAMMERSTEIN II
Music by RICHARD RODGERS

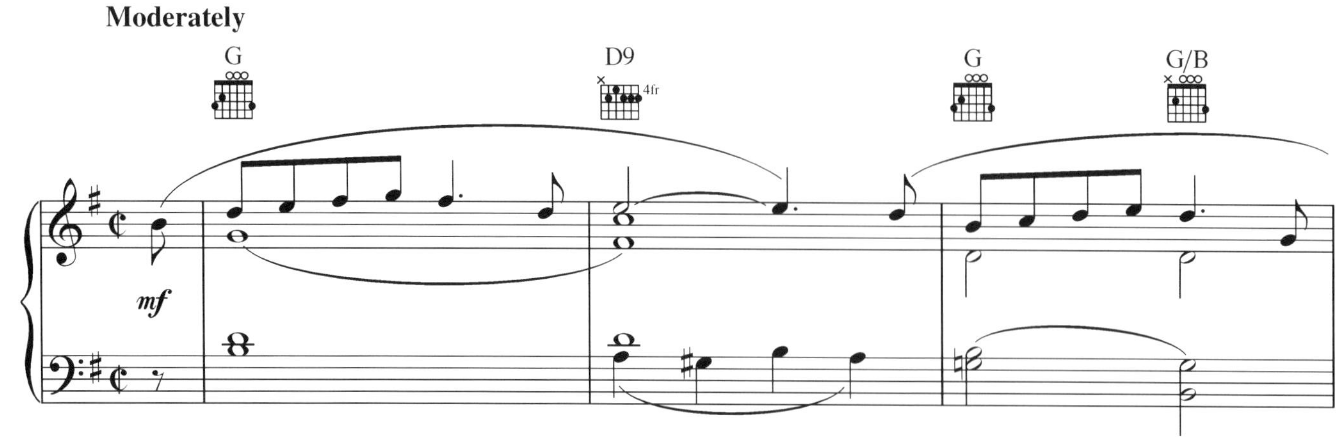

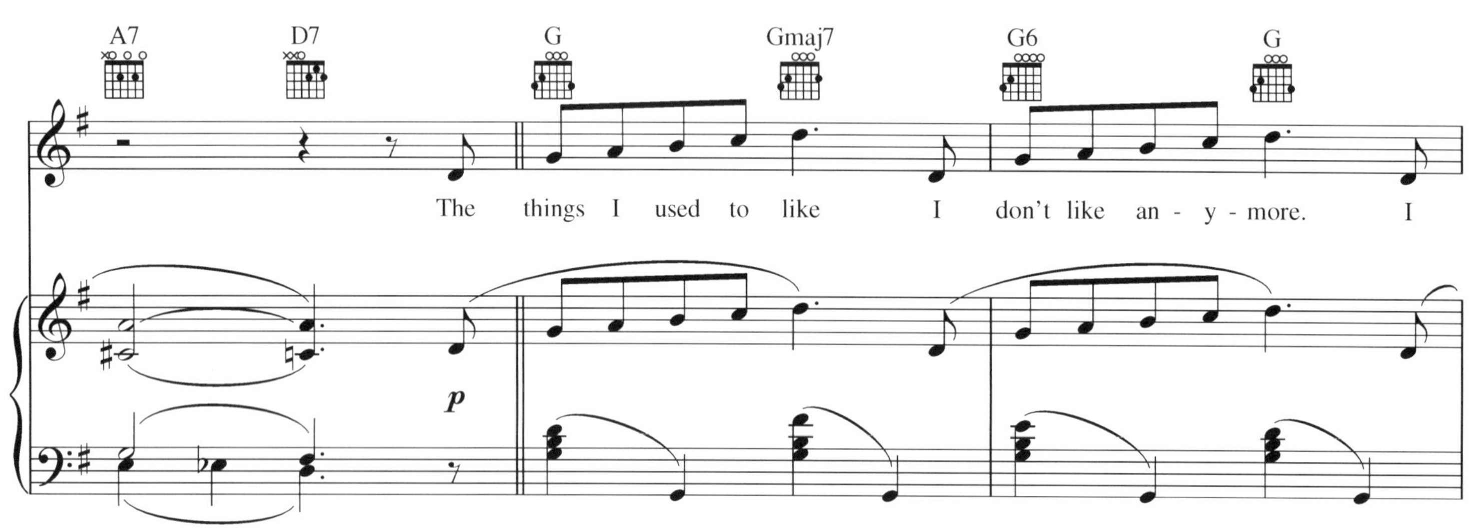

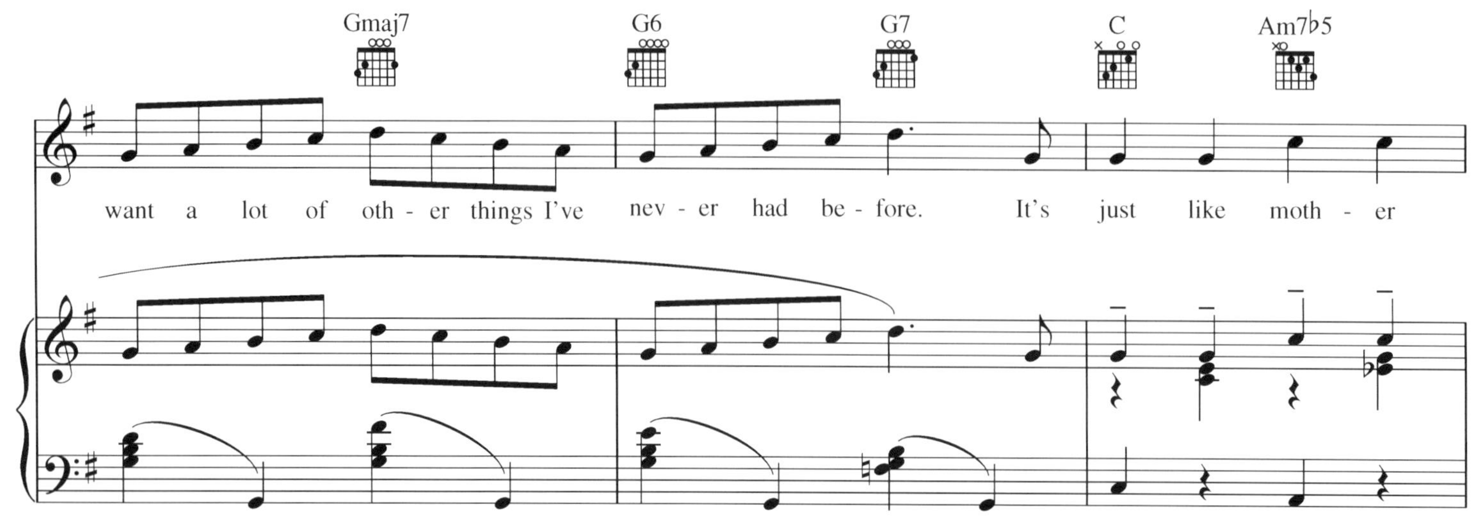

G/D Am7 D7 G6 G
says, I "sit a - round and mope" Pre -
C Am7♭5 G/D Am7 D7
tend - ing I am won - der - ful and know - ing I'm a
G6 G G6 G
dope. I'm as
Refrain (gracefully)
G Gmaj7
rest - less as a wil - low in a
p - mf
G Gmaj7 Dm7 G7
wind - storm, I'm as jump - y as a pup - pet on a string. I'd

C
Cdim7
G/B
G/D
Am7
D7
say that I had spring fe - ver, But I know it is - n't
Gmaj7
G6
G
Gmaj7
G
spring. I am star - ry - eyed and vague - ly dis - con - tent - ed, Like a
Gmaj7
Dm7
G7
C
Cdim7
night - in - gale with - out a song to sing. Oh, why should I have spring
G/B
G/D
Am7
D7
G
C
fe - ver When it is - n't e - ven spring? I keep wish - ing I were

Dm7 Dm7/G Dm7 G7♭5(♯9) G7 C
some - where else, walk - ing down a strange new street,
F♯m7 B7 Em/G A7 G D7 G D7
Hear - ing words that I have nev - er heard from a (man / girl) I've yet to meet. I'm as
cresc.
mf
p
G Gmaj7 G Gmaj7
bus - y as a spi - der spin - ning day - dreams, I'm as gid - dy as a ba - by on a
Dm7 G7 C Cdim7 G/B G/D
swing. I have - n't seen a cro - cus or a rose - bud, or a

C6 D9 B7 E7♭9 A7

rob - in on the wing, But I feel so gay in a

D9 G7 A7

mel - an - cho - ly way that it might as well be spring. It

G/D D7sus D7 1 G Em

might ___ as well ___ be spring!

C D7 2 G C6 G

I'm as spring! ___

mf *mf*

IT'S A MOST UNUSUAL DAY

from A DATE WITH JUDY

Words by HAROLD ADAMSON
Music by JIMMY McHUGH

A11 A7 D G6 Gdim
what was a - head. I took one good look at the
F♯m7 Bm7 C9 A7 D7sus
sun and was I the luck - i - est one.
D7 F♯/G G C♯dim G/D Am7
It's a most un - u - su - al day,
most un - u - su - al sky,
D7 F♯/G G C6/G G/D C♯dim G/D Am7
feel like throw - ing my wor - ries a - way,
not a sign of a cloud pass - ing by,
4fr
4fr

D7
G/B
C6
C♯dim7
as an old na - tive born Cal - i - for - nian would
and if I want to sing, throw my heart in the
1
G/D
Bm
Em7
A7
D7
say, it's a most un - u - su - al day. There's a
2
G/D
G♯dim7
Am7
D7
G
C6/G
G
Em7
D♯m7
6fr
ring, it's a most un - u - su - al day. There are
Dm7
G7
Cmaj7
C6
Em7
D♯m7
6fr
peo - ple meet - ing peo - ple, there is

Dm7
G7
Cmaj7
C6
F♯m7
Fm7
sun - shine ev - 'ry - where. There are
Em7
A7
Dmaj7
D6
Am7/D
G/D
peo - ple greet - ing peo - ple and a feel - ing of
D7
Am7/D
D7
F♯/G
G
spring in the air. It's a most un -
C♯dim
G/D
Am7
D7
F♯/G
G
C6/G
u - su - al time, I keep feel - ing my

G/D
C♯dim
4fr
G/D
Am7
D7
G/B
tem - p'ra - ture climb.
If my heart won't be -
C6
C♯dim7
G/D
Bm
Em7
have in the u - su - al way, well, there's on - ly one thing to
A7
D7
G
D7
G
say, it's a most un - u - su - al, most un -
D7
G
D7
G
u - su - al, most un - u - su - al day.

IT NEVER ENTERED MY MIND

Words by LORENZ HART
Music by RICHARD RODGERS

A7
D7
G7
walk in a daze now, I never go to shows at night, But just to matinees now.
Csus
C
Cm6
C9
I see the show and home I go.
poco rit.
Refrain (slowly, with warm expression)
F
Am
Once I laughed when I heard you saying That I'd be playing
p - mf a tempo
solitaire, Uneasy in my easy chair.

Gm7 Gm Eb7 C7 F Am

It nev - er en - tered my mind. __ Once you told me

mf *p*

F Am F Am F Am

I was mis - tak - en That I'd a - wak - en with the sun __

F Am F Am Gm7 F

And or - der or - ange juice for one. __ It nev - er en - tered my mind. __

Am/C E+/B C7 F6 Gm7 Bb/C C7 Fmaj7 F6

__ You have what __ I lack my - self, __

mf *mp*

Gm7 B♭/C C7 F6 C7 F A♭dim7 C7 B♭/D Am/C
And now I e - ven have to scratch my back my - self.
mf
marcato
B♭/D Am/C C7 F Am F Am F Am
Once you warned me That if you scorned me, I'd sing the maid - en's
p
F Am F Am Am7♭5 D7 Gm C7
pray'r a - gain. And wish that you were there a - gain To get in - to my
3fr
Fmaj7 B♭6 C7 F6 G7 C7
hair a - gain. It nev - er en - tered my mind.
1
2
mf
p

IT'S EASY TO REMEMBER

from the Paramount Picture MISSISSIPPI

Words by LORENZ HART
Music by RICHARD RODGERS

Moderately

Fm7 B♭7 E♭(add9) E♭6 Fm7 B♭7

p

E♭maj7 E♭6 Fm7 B♭7 E♭ Fm7 B♭7

mp

With you ___ I owned the earth. With you ___ I ruled cre -

E♭6 E♭7 A♭ Fm7♭5 E♭ A♭m

a - tion. No you, ___ and what's it worth? It's just an im - i -

rall.

Refrain *(slowly and expressively)*

F7 B♭7 N.C. Fm7 B♭7 E♭ Fm7 B♭7

p *mp*

ta - tion. ___ Your sweet ex - pres - sion, ___ the smile you gave me, ___ the way you looked when we

E♭ A♭ E♭/G Fm7 E♭/B♭ B♭9
met. It's eas - y to re - mem - ber but so hard to for -
E♭ Fm7 B♭7 E♭ Fm7 B♭7
get. I hear you whis - per, "I'll al-ways love you." I know it's o - ver, and
E♭ A♭ E♭/G Fm7 E♭/B♭ B♭9
yet, it's eas - y to re - mem - ber but so hard to for -
E♭ E♭7sus E♭7 A♭maj7 A♭6 B♭m7 E♭7
get. So I must dream to have your hand ca - ress me, fin - gers press me

Abmaj7 Ab6 Abm7 Db7 Gbmaj7 Gb6 Bb/F Cm/F F7

tight. I'd rath - er dream than have that lone - ly feel - ing steal - ing through the

Bb Bb7 Fm7 Bb7 Eb

night. Each lit - tle mo - ment is clear be - fore me, and though it

Fm7 Bb7 Eb Ab Eb/G Db9

brings me re - gret, it's eas - y to re - mem - ber and

1 Eb/Bb Bb9 Eb N.C. 2 Eb/Bb Bb9 Eb Ab6/9 Eb

so hard to for - get. Your sweet ex - so hard to for - get.

mp *rall.*

JUNE IN JANUARY

from the Paramount Picture HERE IS MY HEART

Words and Music by LEO ROBIN
and RALPH RAINGER

C7
Fm
just white blos - soms that fall from a - bove,
Bb7
Fm7
Bb7
Eb
3fr
and here is the rea - son, my dear, your mag - ic - al charms.
G7#5
G7
Cm
3fr
Cdim7
The night is cold,
R.H.
Cm
3fr
Fm6/C
Cm
3fr
the trees are bare, but I can
R.H.

Cm7
F9
B♭7
B♭7♯5(♭9)
feel the scent of ros - es in the air. It's
E♭
C7
Fm
June in Jan - u - ar - y be - cause I'm in
B♭7
Fm7
Fm7/B♭
B♭7
love, but on - ly be - cause I'm in love with
E♭
G♭
B♭7sus
B♭7
B♭7♯5(♭9)
E♭
A♭6
E♭6
you. It's you.

THE LADY IS A TRAMP

Words by LORENZ HART
Music by RICHARD RODGERS

C9
F
Fm6
both - er with peo - ple I hate,
C
C+
F6
G9
9fr
C
G7
That's why the la - dy is a tramp.
mf
C
Cm7
3fr
Dm7
G7
I don't like crap - games with Bar - ons and Earls,
C
Cm7
3fr
Dm7
G7
Won't go to Har - lem in er - mine and pearls.

C
Cmaj7
C9
F
Fm6
Won't dish the dirt with the rest of the girls,
C
C+
F
G7
C
N.C.
That's why the la - dy is a tramp.
I like the
Fmaj7
G7
Em7
Am
free fresh wind in my hair,
mf
Dm7
G7
C
A7
D7
G7
Life with - out care.
I'm broke,
it's oke.

C
Cm7
3fr
Dm
E7
Hate Cal - i - for - nia, It's cold and it's damp,
p
Am
C+
Am7
1
D7
G7
C
Am
Dm7
G7
That's why the la - dy is a tramp.
mf
2
D7
D7♭5/A♭
G7
C
Cmaj7
la - dy is a tramp.
f
Cm7
3fr
Dm/C
Fm/C
G7
C
sf

THE LADY'S IN LOVE WITH YOU

from the Paramount Picture SOME LIKE IT HOT

Words by FRANK LOESSER
Music by BURTON LANE

E7♭9
E7
Am
Am9/G
Am6/F♯
B7♭9
B7
Why wait for her to say that she a -
Em
A7(add13)
A7♯5
A7
dores you?
Long be - fore the first kiss
A7(add13)
A7♯5
A7
D9♯5
D7♯5(♭9)
D7♯5
N.C.
have you ev - er seen this?
If there's a
A9/E
Am7/D
D9
gleam in here eye each time she straight - ens your tie,

G
G+/D
G
D+
G6
D9♯5
4fr
you'll know the la - dy's in love with you.
G6
N.C.
A9/E
5fr
Am7/D
D9
If she can dress for a date with - out that wait - ing you hate
G
G+/D
G
D+
G6
D9♯5
it means the la - dy's in love with you.
G6
G7
Dm7
G7
Dm7
Dm9
3fr
And when your friends ask you o - ver to join their ta - ble
3

G9♯5 G7 C Cm6
but she picks that far a - way booth for two,
3
D7 N.C. A9/E Am7/D D9
Well, sir, here's just how it stands, you've got ro - mancc on your hands
5fr 4fr 3fr
E7 D/F♯ E7/G♯ E7/A Am Am7 D7♭9
be - cause the la - dy's in love with
1
G Em7 A9 D9 N.C.
you. If there's a
2
G Em7 A9 A♭9♯5 G6
you.

LOLLIPOPS AND ROSES

1
2
Gm7
F/A
D7
D7
Em7
lol - li - pops and lol - li - pops and ros - es.
lol - li - pops and lol - li - pops and ros - es. We try
A7
Dmaj7
D6
E♭m7
A♭7
act - ing grown - up, but as a
D♭maj7
D♭6
Fm7
B♭7
E♭maj7
rule we're all lit - tle chil - dren
E♭6
Dm7
G7♭9
Gm7
C7
fresh from school. So

Gm7 C7 Am7 Dm Cdim7
car - ry her books; that's how it starts. Four - teen or
Gm7/B♭ Am7 D7 Gm7 C7♭9
for - ty, they're kids in their hearts. Keep them hand - y,
Fmaj7 Gm7♭5 F/A Gm7 F/A
flow - ers and can - dy, ros - es and lol - li - pops and lol - li - pops
D7 Gm7 C7 F F6
and ros - es.

LOVER

from the Paramount Picture LOVE ME TONIGHT

Words by LORENZ HART
Music by RICHARD RODGERS

D
D6
Em7
A7
D
Since you took con - trol of my life you have be -
C♯7
F♯m
Bm
Em7
come the whole of my life. When you are a - way it's
A7
F♯m
D6
E7
A7
aw - ful and when you are with me it's worse.
D
G♯m7
C♯7
Gm7
Lov - er, when I'm near you and I hear you
4fr
3fr

C7 F♯m7 B7 Fm7 B♭7
speak my name soft - ly in my
Em7 A7 D D7 G
ear you breathe a flame.
A7 D G♯m7 C♯7
Lov - er, when we're danc - ing, keep on
Lov - er, it's im - mor - al, but why
Gm7 C7 F♯m7 B7 Fm7
glanc - ing in my eyes till love's
quar - rel with our bliss when two
4fr
3fr

B♭7
Em7
A7
D
own en - tranc - ing mu - sic dies.
lips of cor - al want to kiss?
F♯
G♯m7
4fr
All of my fu - ture is in you.
I say "The Dev - il is in you,"
C♯7
F♯
G♯m7
4fr
C♯7
Your ev - 'ry plan I de - sign.
and to re - sist you I try;
A
Bm7
2fr
E7
Em7/A
Prom - ise you'll al - ways con - tin - ue to be mine.
but if you did - n't con - tin - ue I would die!

A7 D G♯m7 C♯7
Lov - er, please be ten - der. When you're
Gm7 C7 F♯m7 B7 Fm7
ten - der, fears de - part. Lov - er,
B♭7 Em7 A7
I sur - ren - der to my
1
D6 Bm
heart.
Em7 A7
2
D6 Bm Em7 A7 D
heart.
8vb

LOVE IS JUST AROUND THE CORNER

from the Paramount Picture HERE IS MY HEART

Words and Music by LEO ROBIN
and LEWIS E. GENSLER

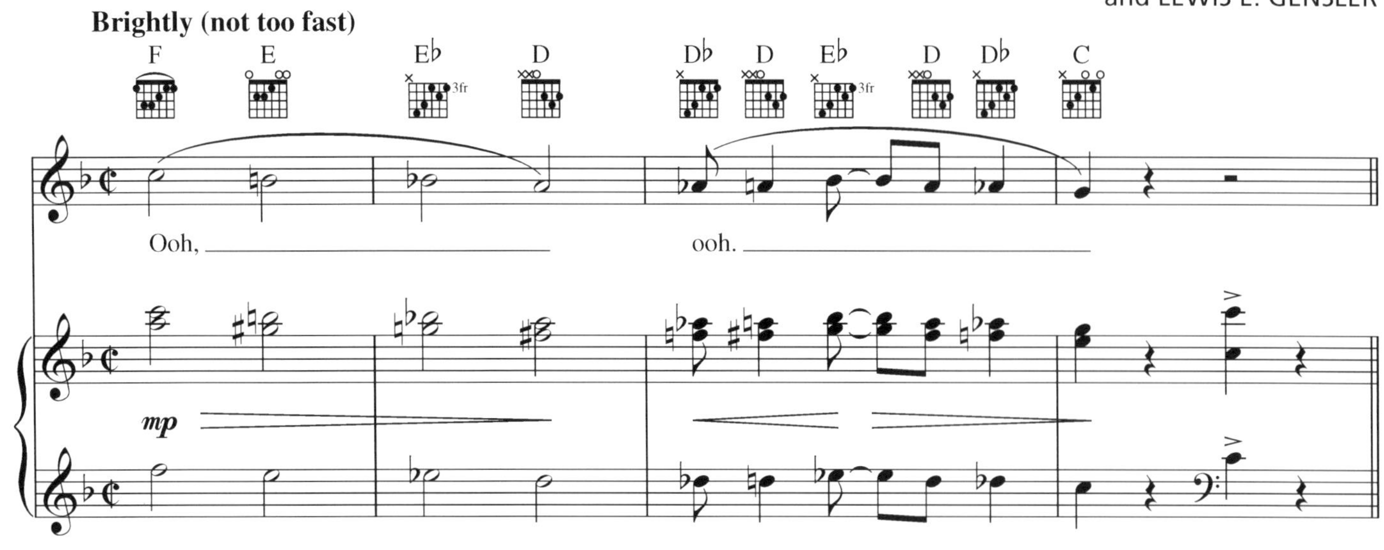

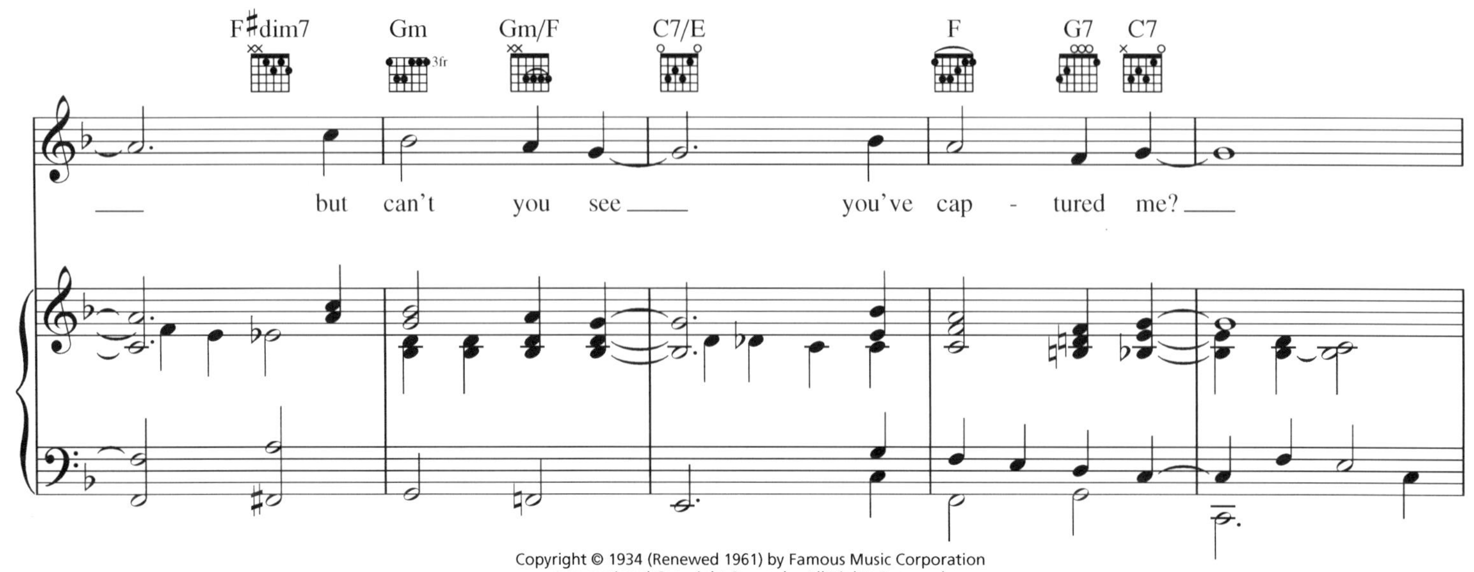

F C7 F C9 F C7 F F♯dim7
Be-ing so glam-or-ous, can't you be am-o-rous just with me? Make it
C/G C/E E♭dim7 G7/D G7♭5/D♭ C7 B♭/C C7 Cmaj7♯5
soon, take a look at the moon.
G7 C7 F G7 C7 F
Love is just a-round the cor-ner, an-y co-zy lit-tle cor-ner.
mp - mf
G7 C7 F Cm6/E♭ D7 G9 C7 F
Love is just a-round the cor-ner when I'm a-round you.

G7 C7 F G7 C7
I'm a sen - ti - men - tal mourn - er, and I could - n't be for -
F G7 C7 F Cm6/E♭ D7 G9 C7
lorn - er when you keep me on a cor - ner just wait - ing for
F A7 Dm A7
you. Ve - nus de Mi - lo was not - ed for her
Dm Dm7♭5 G7 Gdim7 G7 Gdim7
charms, But strict - ly be - tween us, you're cut - er than Ve - nus and

G7
C7
G7
C7
what's more, you got arms. So let's go cud - dle in a
8va
F
G7
C7
F
cor - ner, an - y co - zy lit - tle cor - ner.
G7
C7
F
Am7/E♭
D7
G9
C7
1
F
G9
C7
Love is just a - round the cor - ner, and I'm a - round you.
2
F
E
E♭
D
C♯
D
E♭
E
F
F6
3fr
you. Ooh, ooh, ooh.
mp
pp

LOVE LETTERS

Theme from the Paramount Picture LOVE LETTERS

Words by EDWARD HEYMAN
Music by VICTOR YOUNG

Bm
D7/A
G
deep in my heart I know that you
Gm6
3fr
D/A
Em7
G/A
3fr
A7
love me. You love me be - cause you told me
D
Ddim7
D7
G
so!
Love let - ters straight from your
Em/G
Am/G
F♯dim7/G
10fr
heart
keep us so near
while a -
3

Gmaj7
C♯m7♭5
F♯7♭9
F♯7
part,
I'm not a - lone in the
Bm
Dm/A
E7
Am
Fdim7/A
E7/A
night
when I can have all the
Am
Cm6/G
D7
G
love you write.
I mem - o -
Em/G
rize ev - 'ry line.

Am/G
F♯dim7/G
10fr
G7
G7♭9
I kiss the name that you sign,
Cmaj7
Am7♭5
D7
G/D
G/B
And, dar - ling, then I read a - gain right from the
B♭dim7
Am7
C/D
D7♭9(13)
4fr
start love let - ters straight from your
G6
B♭dim7
Am7
D9sus
5fr
D7
heart.
C6/G
heart.

LOVER MAN
(Oh, Where Can You Be?)

By JIMMY DAVIS,
ROGER RAMIREZ and JIMMY SHERMAN

Dm G7 Dm G7
I don't know why, but I'm feel - ing so sad.
C9 Gm7 C9 C7 F7♯9
7fr
I long to try some-thing I've nev - er had,
nev - er had no kiss - in',
B♭7 E♭7 Gm7♭5/D♭ C9 Gm7
3fr
oh, what I've been miss - in'.
Lov - er man, oh where can you
F A7 Dm G7 Dm G7
be?
The night is cold, and I'm so all a - lone,

C9 Gm7 C9 C7 F7♯9
7fr
I'd give my soul just to call you my own, _ got a moon a - bove me,
B♭7 E♭7 Gm7♭5/D♭ C9 Gm7
3fr
but no one to love me. Lov - er man, oh where can you
F B♭ Am Am7♭5 D7 C/D Cm/D
3fr
be? I've heard it said that the thrill of ro - mance can
3
G A9/G E♭7/G G D7 Gm Gm7♭5
5fr
3fr
be like a heav - en - ly dream, I go to bed with a
3

C7
F
E♭7
Em7♭5
A7♯5
A7
pray'r that you'll make love to me, strange as it seems,
Dm
G7
Dm
G7
C9
Gm7
some day we'll meet and you'll dry all my tears, then whis - per sweet lit - tle
C9
C7
F7♯9
7fr
B♭7
things in my ears, hug - gin' and a kiss - in', oh, what we've been miss - in'.
E♭7
B♭m/D♭
C9
Gm7
1
F
A7♯5
A7
2
F
F6/9
Lov - er man, oh where can you be? be?

LULLABY OF BIRDLAND

Words by GEORGE DAVID WEISS
Music by GEORGE SHEARING

C9
F♯m7♭5
B7
in a phrase, how I feel!
Em
C♯m7♭5
F♯7♭9
B7♭9
Em7
Cmaj7
3fr
Have you ev - er heard two tur - tle - doves bill and coo
Am7
D9
4fr
Bm7
Em7
when they love? That's the kind of mag - ic
Am7
D7♭9
4fr
G
D7
G
mu - sic we make with our lips when we kiss!

E9 E7♭9 Am Am7

And there's a weep - y old wil - low,

D9 D7♭9 G E9 E7♭9

he real - ly knows how to cry. That's how I'd cry in my pil -

Am Am7 D9 D7♭9 G B7

low if you should tell me fare - well and good - bye.

Em C♯m7♭5 F♯7♭9 B7♭9 Em7 Cmaj7

Lull - a - by of Bird - land, whis - per low, kiss me sweet

Am7
D9
4fr
Bm7
Em7
and we'll go fly - in' high in Bird - land,
Am7
D7♭9
G
1
C9
F♯m7♭5
high in the sky up a - bove all be - cause
B7
2
we're in love.
all be - cause
D9
D7♭9
G6
C9
Am7
A♭9
G6/9
we're in love.

LUSH LIFE

Words and Music by
BILLY STRAYHORN

D♭
C♭7
D♭maj7
C♭7
girls I knew had sad and sul - len gray fac - es, with dis - tin -
D♭maj7
C♭7
D♭maj7
E♭m7
F♭maj7
G♭m7
gue trac - es, that used to be there you could see where they'd been
A♭m7
D9
D♭6
D9
D♭6
C7
washed a - way by too man - y through the day twelve o' - clock tails. Then
Fm
Fm6
Fm7
Fm6
Fm
you came a - long with your si - ren song to tempt me to mad - ness,

Gm7
C7♭9
Fm
Fm6
Fm7
Fm6
I thought for a while that your poig - nant smile was
D♭
Edim7
E♭m7
A♭9
C♭9
tinged with the sad - ness of a great love for me.
B♭9
B♭7♭9
E♭m7
A7♭5
Ah, yes I was wrong, a - gain I was
E♭m7
A♭7
A♭7♯5
D♭
D9
wrong!
Life is lone - ly a -

D♭ D9 D♭6 C7♯11 B7♭9
gain, and on - ly last year ev - 'ry-thing seemed so
E E♭ D D♭ D7 D♭ D7
sure. Now life is aw - ful a - gain, a trough - ful of
D♭ D♭9 C7♭9 F F♭ E♭ A♭6 E♭7♯5
hearts could on - ly be a bore. A week in Pa - ris will
A♭6 Em9 A7♭9 D Dm7 C6 C♭7 B♭9 A7 A♭9
ease the bite of it. All I care is to smile in spite of it.

D♭ D7 D♭ D7 D♭6 C7♯11 B7♭9
I'll for - get you, I will, while yet you are still burn - ing in - side my
B♭7 B♭9 B♭7♭9 E♭m7 G♭m9 G♭m6 A9 A♭9
brain. Ro - mance is mush, sti - fling those who strive, I'll
D♭maj9 D♭m9 G♭7♭9 C♭maj9 C♭6 Fm11 B♭7♭9 E♭m7 G♭m9 G♭m6
live a lush life in some small dive, and there I'll be, while I
A7♯5 A♭9 F♭ E♭6 Dmaj7 G9 D♭6 D9 D♭maj7
rot with the rest of those whose lives are lone - ly too.

MEDITATION
(Meditacão)

Music by ANTONIO CARLOS JOBIM
Original Words by NEWTON MENDONÇA
English Words by NORMAN GIMBEL

Fm6
Em7
A7♯5
and the thought of you hold - ing me near makes my lone -
and the sad - ness that miss - ing you brings soon is gone
Dm7
G7♯5
Fmaj7
- li - ness soon dis - ap - pear.
and this heart of mine sings.
Yes,
Fm6
Em7
I love you so and that for me is all
E♭dim
6fr
Dm7
G7♯5
C
I need to know.
I

B7
will wait for you 'til the sun
C
Em7
A7#5
falls from out of the sky for what else can I do?
Dm7
Fm7
Fm6
I will wait for you, med - i - tat -
Em7
A7#5
Dm7
G7b9
C
Bb9
Cmaj7
- ing how sweet life will be when you come back to me.

MISTY

Words by JOHNNY BURKE
Music by ERROLL GARNER

B♭m7 E♭7♭9 A♭maj7 A♭m D♭9
thou-sand vi-o-lins be-gin to play, Or it might be the sound of your hel-lo, That
E♭maj7 Cm Fm7 B♭7♭9 E♭ Cm7 Fm7 B♭7♭9
mu - sic I hear, I get mist-y, the mo-ment you're near.
E♭6 B♭m7 E♭7
You can say that you're lead-ing me on, But it's just what I
A♭maj7 A♭6 Am7
want you to do, Don't you no-tice how hope-less-ly I'm lost,

D7
F7
B♭7
Edim
Fm7
B♭7♭9
B♭9
That's why I'm fol - low - ing you.
On my
E♭maj7
B♭m7
E♭7♭9
A♭maj7
own, would I wan - der through this won - der - land a - lone,
Nev - er know - ing my
A♭m
D♭9
E♭maj7
Cm
Fm7
B♭7♭9
right foot from my left, My hat from my glove, I'm too mist - y and too much in
1
E♭
E9♭5
Fm7
B♭7♯5
B♭9
love. Look at
2
E♭
A♭maj7
Gm7
E7
E♭maj7
love.

MONA LISA

from the Paramount Picture CAPTAIN CAREY, U.S.A.

Words and Music by JAY LIVINGSTON
and RAY EVANS

E♭
3fr
Li - sa, Mo - na Li - sa, men have named you. You're so
Fm7
B♭
Fm
like the la - dy with the mys - tic smile. Is it on - ly 'cause you're lone - ly they have
3
B♭7
E♭
3fr
blamed you for that Mo - na Li - sa strange - ness in your smile? Do you
3
smile to tempt a lov - er, Mo - na Li - sa, or is

A♭
A♭m
this your way to hide a bro - ken heart? Man - y dreams have been brought to your
E♭
B♭7
E♭
E♭7
door - step. They just lie there, and they die there. Are you
A♭
E♭
warm, are you real, Mo - na Li - sa, or just a
B♭7
1 E♭
2 E♭
cold and lone - ly, love - ly work of art? Mo - na art?

MOON RIVER

from the Paramount Picture BREAKFAST AT TIFFANY'S

Words by JOHNNY MERCER
Music by HENRY MANCINI

C7/G
F
B♭9♯11
Am
Am7/G
5fr
mak - er, you heart - break - er, wher - ev - er you're
F♯m7♭5
4fr
B7
Em7
A7
Dm7
G9
9fr
C
go - in', I'm go - in' your way. Two
Am
F
C/E
F
drift - ers, off to see the world. There's such a lot of
C/E
Bm7♭5
E7
Am
world to see. We're af -

Am/G
F♯m7♭5
F13
C/E
ter the same rain - bow's end.
F
C/E
F
C/E
wait - in' 'round the bend, my Huck - le - ber - ry friend,
Am
Dm7
G9
1
C
Moon Riv - er and me.
2
A♭maj7
D♭maj7
C
me.
rall.

MORE THAN YOU KNOW

Words by WILLIAM ROSE and EDWARD ELISCU
Music by VINCENT YOUMANS

C6
G7♯5
C9sus
C9
C7
Fmaj7
A7♭9
5fr
right, wheth - er you're wrong. { man / girl } o' my heart, I'll string a -
F6
Fm6
C/E
A7
D9
4fr
G7
long. You need me so more than you'll ev - er
C
F6
C
F♯m7♭5
4fr
B7
Em
know. Lov - ing you the way that I do, there's
Am6
Am7
Bm7
Em
Am7♭5
D7
noth - ing I can do a - bout it, Lov - ing may be

G Em7 A7 Am7/D D7 G7 Gdim
all you can give but, hon - ey, I can't live with - out it. (Hum)
G7 G7♯5 C6 G7♯5 C9sus C9 C7
Oh, how I'd cry, oh, how I'd cry, if you got
Fmaj7 A7♭9 F6 Fm6 C/E A7 D9 G9
tired and said "good - bye," more than I'd show more than you'd ev - er
1 C G9sus G9 G7♯5
know. More than you
2 Cmaj7
know.
mf

MOONLIGHT BECOMES YOU

from the Paramount Picture ROAD TO MOROCCO

Words by JOHNNY BURKE
Music by JAMES VAN HEUSEN

Bm7
D/E
E7
A
Gm7/C
C7
learn to look so love - ly?
F
F♯dim7
Gm7
C7
F
F/A
A♭dim7
Moon - light be - comes you. It goes with your
Gm7
C7♯5
Am7
D7
Gm7
C7♭9
hair. You cer - tain - ly know the right thing to
F
Gm7
C7♭9
F
F♯dim7
Gm7
C7
wear.
Moon - light be - comes you. I'm

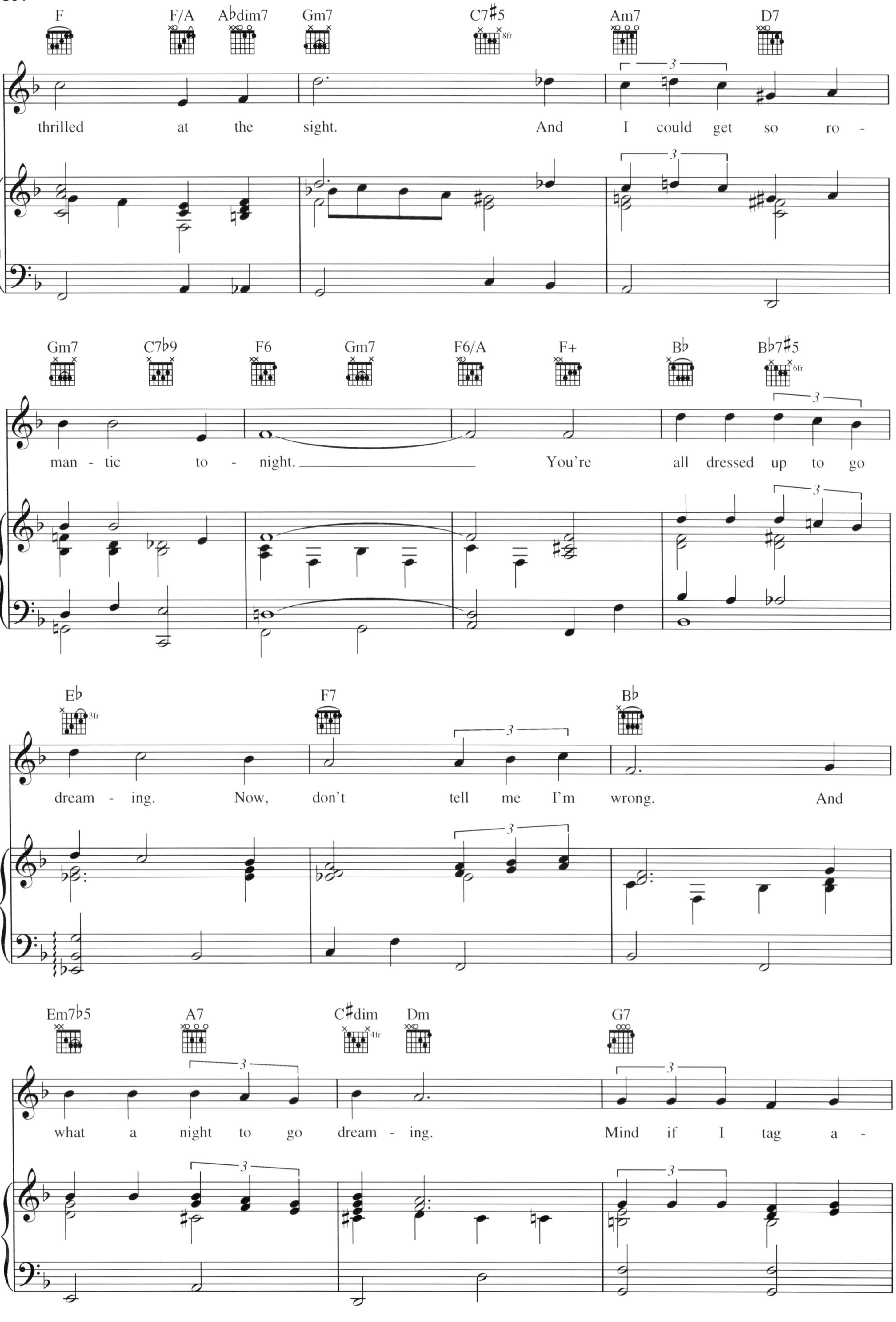
F F/A A♭dim7 Gm7 C7♯5 Am7 D7
8fr
thrilled at the sight. And I could get so ro -
Gm7 C7♭9 F6 Gm7 F6/A F+ B♭ B♭7♯5
6fr
man - tic to - night. You're all dressed up to go
E♭ F7 B♭
3fr
dream - ing. Now, don't tell me I'm wrong. And
Em7♭5 A7 C♯dim Dm G7
4fr
what a night to go dream - ing. Mind if I tag a -

Gm7/C
C7♯5
8fr
F
F♯dim7
Gm7
C7
long? If I say I love you, I
F
F/A
A♭dim7
Gm7
C7♯5
8fr
Am7
D7
3
want you to know it's not just be - cause there's
Gm7
C7
A7
D7
G7
Gm7/C
C7
3
moon - light. Al - though, moon - light be - comes you
1
F
Gm7/C
C7♯5(♭9)
so.
2
F
B♭m6
6fr
F6
so.

MY FAVORITE THINGS

from THE SOUND OF MUSIC

Lyrics by OSCAR HAMMERSTEIN II
Music by RICHARD RODGERS

Em
Cream - col - ored po - nies and crisp ap - ple
mf
mp
Cmaj7
stru - dels, Door - bells and sleigh - bells and schnitz - el with noo - dles,
Am7
D7
G/B
C/E
G/D
Wild geese that fly with the moon on their wings, These are a
C
F♯m7♭5
4fr
B7
E
few of my fa - vor - ite things.
f

A
Girls in white dress - es with blue sat - in sash - es, Snow - flakes that
mf
Am7
D7
stay on my nose and eye - lash - es, Sil - ver white win - ters that
G/B
C/E
G/D
C
F♯m7♭5
4fr
B7♭9
melt in - to springs, These are a few of my fa - vor - ite things.
Em
F♯m7♭5
4fr
B7
When the dog bites, When the bee stings,
mf

Em
C
When I'm feel - ing sad, I
sim - ply re - mem - ber my fa - vor - ite things and
A7/C♯
A7
G/D C/D G/D C/D G
D7♭9
D7
G
4fr
then I don't feel so bad.
cresc.
f
C
G/D
D7
G
sf

MY FUNNY VALENTINE

Words by LORENZ HART
Music by RICHARD RODGERS

G
Cm
Fm
made, thy va - cant brow and thy tous - led hair con -
Eb
Cm
ceal thy good in - tent. Thou no - ble, up - right,
Bb7
Cm
G7
G7#5
truth - ful, sin - cere and slight - ly dop - ey gent, you're
Cm
Cm(maj7)
Cm7
my
My
fun - ny val - en - tine, sweet com - ic
p

Cm6
3fr
Fm/C
Fm
val - en - tine, You make me smile with my
Dm7♭5
G7
Fm/A♭
G7
heart.
Cm
3fr
Cm(maj7)
8fr
Cm7
3fr
Your looks are laugh - a - ble, un - pho - to -
F7/C
3fr
Fm/C
Fm7
graph - a - ble, yet you're my fav - 'rite work of

A♭m/C♭
A♭m/F
B♭7
B♭/A♭
E♭/G
B♭7
art. Is your fig - ure less than
mf
E♭/G
B♭7
E♭6/G
B♭7
E♭/G
B♭7
Greek; is your mouth a lit - tle weak, when you
E♭maj7/G
G7
Cm
A♭maj7
A♭6
o - pen it to speak, are you smart?
A♭7
G7
Cm
Cm(maj7)
But don't change a hair for me,
p

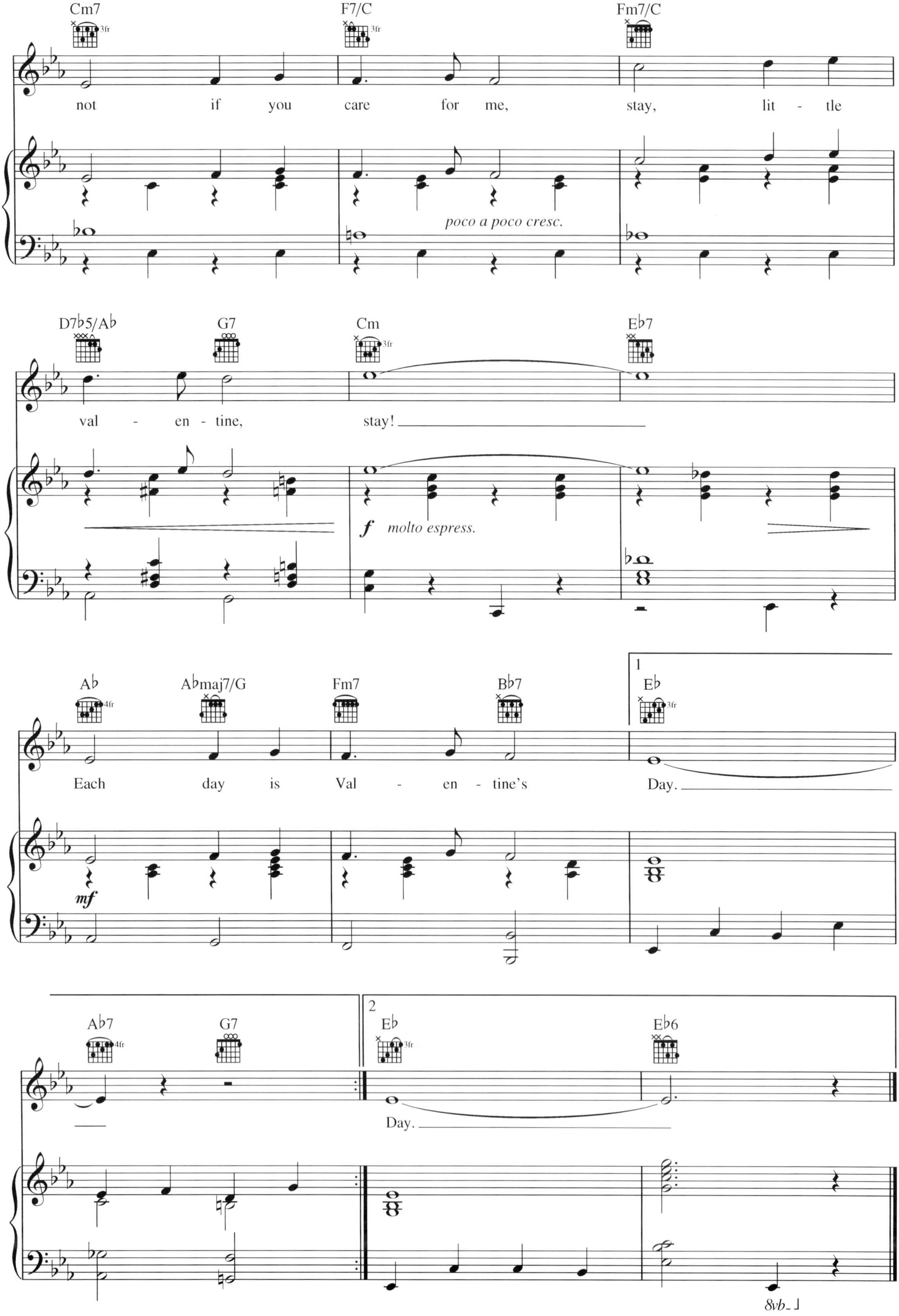
Cm7
3fr
F7/C
3fr
Fm7/C
not if you care for me, stay, lit - tle
poco a poco cresc.
D7♭5/A♭
G7
Cm
3fr
E♭7
val - en - tine, stay!
f
molto espress.
A♭
4fr
A♭maj7/G
Fm7
B♭7
1
E♭
3fr
Each day is Val - en - tine's Day.
mf
A♭7
4fr
G7
2
E♭
3fr
E♭6
Day.
8vb

THE NEARNESS OF YOU

from the Paramount Picture ROMANCE IN THE DARK

Words by NED WASHINGTON
Music by HOAGY CARMICHAEL

F Am7 Gm7 B♭/C C7
you're at a dis - tance, but when you are near, oh
F Fmaj7 Cm7 Cm7/F F7♯5
my! It's not the pale moon that ex - cites me, that
B♭maj7 B♭dim7 B♭m Am7 A♭7
thrills and de - lights me. Oh, no
Gm7 C7 Am7 A♭7
it's just the near - ness of you.

Gm7
C7
Fmaj7
Cm7
Cm7/F
F7♯5
It isn't your sweet con - ver - sa - tion that
Bbmaj7
Bbdim7
Bbm
Am7
Ab7
brings this sen - sa - tion. Oh, no
Gm7
C7
F6
it's just the near - ness of you.
Gm7b5
When you're in my arms

C7♭9 Fmaj7 F7

and I feel you so close to me, all my

B♭maj7 Am7♭5 D7 Gm7 3fr E♭7

wild - est dreams come true.

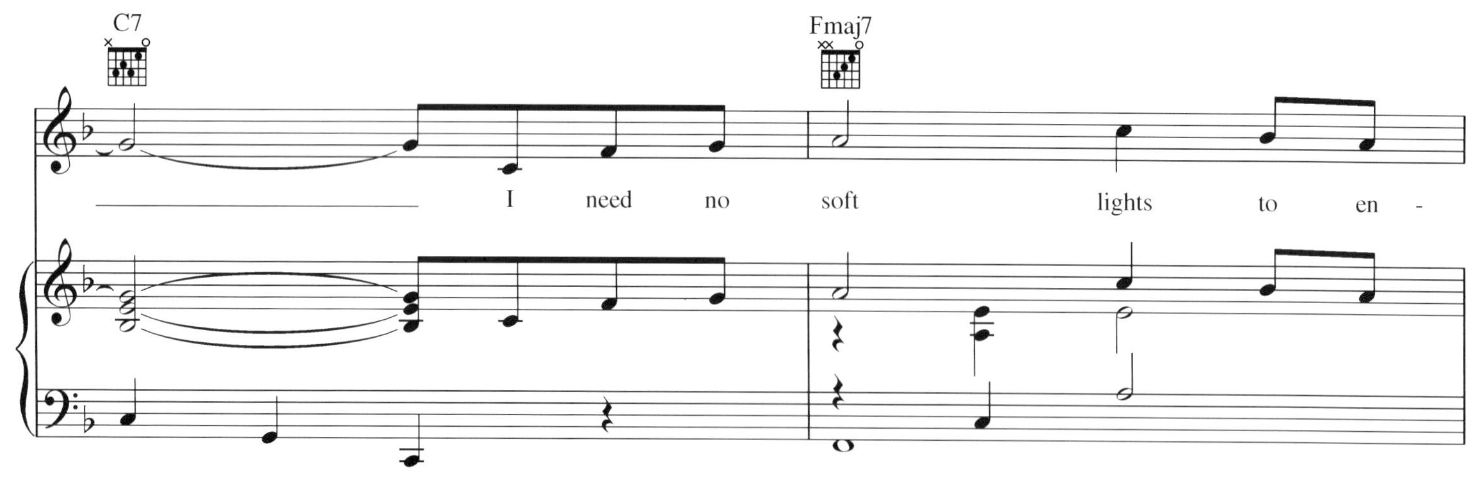

Am7
A♭7
Gm7
C7
right
to hold you ev - er so
Am7♭5
D7♭9
tight,
and to feel in the
Gm7
optional
C7
C7sus
C7
1 F
Dm7
night the near - ness of you.
Gm7
C7
2 F
B♭
B♭m
F6
It's not the
you.

MY HEART STOOD STILL

Words by LORENZ HART
Music by RICHARD RODGERS

A
Bm7/E
E7
C
Ice - land Was my heart's do - main. I
Pla - to, Love, I thought a sin; But
G7
C
C/B♭
Am7
A♭dim7
saw your eyes; Now cas - tles rise in Spain!
since your kiss, I'm read - ing Mis - sus Glyn!
Gm7/C
C7
F
G♯dim7
Gm7
C7
rit.
I took one look at you,
F
F+
Gm7
C7
F
F+
That's all I meant to do; And then my

B♭6
C7
F
Gm7
C7
F
G♯dim7
heart stood still! My feet could
Gm7
C7
F
F+
Gm7
C7
step and walk, My lips could move and talk,
F
F+
B♭6
C7
F
B♭6
F
And yet my heart stood still! Though not a
Fm
C+
C
sin - gle word was spok - en, I could tell you knew, That un - felt

Dm7♭5
G7
C7
clasp of hands Told me so well you knew.
rall.
F
G♯dim7
Gm7
C7
F
F+
I nev - er lived at all Un - til the
a tempo
B♭
Gm7
F/C
C7
thrill of that mo - ment when My heart stood
1
F
Dm6
Am
C7
still.
2
F
still.

MY OLD FLAME

from the Paramount Picture BELLE OF THE NINETIES

Words and Music by ARTHUR JOHNSTON
and SAM COSLOW

G
Bm7♭5
E7
Am
Am7
My old flame, I can't e - ven think of his
F7
D7
G6
C9
F9
B♭6
E♭9
5fr
name but it's fun - ny now and then how my thoughts go flash - ing back a - gain to
D/F♯
A7/E
Am7♭5/E♭
D7
D7♯5
G
my old flame. My old
Bm7♭5
E7
Am
Am7
F7
D7
flame, my new lov - ers all seem so tame, for I

G6
C9
F9
B♭6
E♭9
5fr
D/F♯
A7/E
have - n't met a gent so mag - nif - i - cent or el - e - gant as my old
F7
B♭
Am7♭5
D7♭9
4fr
flame.
I've met so man - y who had fas - ci - nat - in' ways, a
G7♯5
G7
C9sus
C7
fas - ci - nat - in' gaze in their eyes;
F9
D7
Gsus
some who took me up to the skies.
But

A7
D7
D7♯5(♭9)
G
their at-tempts at love were on-ly im-i-ta-tions of my old
Bm7♭5
E7
Am
Am7
F7
D7
flame. I can't e-ven think of his name, but I'll
G6
C9
F9
B♭6
E♭9
nev-er be the same un-til I dis-cov-er what be-came of
Am
D7♯5(♭9)
G6
G
Am/D
Dm7
D7♯5
G6
G
my old flame. flame.

MY ROMANCE

Words by LORENZ HART
Music by RICHARD RODGERS

C♯m7♭5
D/C
C♯m7♭5
D/C
G7/B
Dm7
We don't need that flow - 'ry fuss, no sir, Ma - dam, not for
Dm7/G
G7
Refrain (smoothly, with expression)
C
us. My ro - mance does - n't have to have a
p - mf
F
C
Am
Cmaj7/G
moon in the sky, my ro - mance does - n't
F
C/E
Dm7
G7
Cmaj7
C6
need a blue la - goon stand - ing by; no
mf

F
C
C9
F
C
month of May, no twin - kling stars, no
F♯m7
B7
Em
Am
G/D
D7
G7sus
G7
hide - a - way, no soft gui - tars. My ro -
p
C
F
mance does - n't need a cas - tle ris - ing in
C
Am
Cmaj7/G
F
C/E
Spain, nor a dance to a con - stant - ly sur -

Dm7
G7
Cmaj7
C6
C7
F
A7
pris - ing re - frain. Wide a - wake I can
cresc.
Dm
E7
A7
D7
make my most fan - tas - tic dreams come true; my ro -
mf
C/G
Am
Dm7
G7
1 C
mance does - n't need a thing but you.
f
dim.
D7
G7
2 C6
My ro - you.
mf

MY SILENT LOVE

Words by EDWARD HEYMAN
Music by DANA SUESSE

Fm6
Db7
C7
Fm
C7
You and I are miles a - part,
I've al - ways known it.
Fm/Ab
C7/G
Fm
C7
Fm
Abm6
Bb7
I just make my smiles a part of the game that I must play.
Eb
Bb+
Eb6
I reach for you like I'd reach for a star,
Gm7b5
C7
Fm
Abm
Bb7
Eb
wor - ship - ping you from a - far,
liv - ing with my si - lent love.

A♭m
B♭7♯5
E♭
B♭+
I'm like a flame dy - ing out in the
E♭6
Gm7♭5
C7
Fm
rain, on - ly the ash - es re - main,
A♭m
B♭7
E♭
E♭7
smoul - d'ring like my si - lent love.
A♭
A♭m
E♭/B♭
E♭6
How I long to tell all the things I have planned.

A♭
Fm7♭5
F7
B♭7
Still, it's wrong to tell, you would not un - der - stand.
E♭
B♭+
E♭6
You'll go a - long nev - er dream - ing I care,
Gm7♭5
C7
Fm
A♭m
B♭7
lov - ing some - bod - y some - where, leav - ing me my si - lent
1
E♭
Cm7
F7
B♭7
love.
2
E♭
A♭m6
E♭
love.

THE NIGHT HAS A THOUSAND EYES

Theme from the Paramount Picture THE NIGHT HAS A THOUSAND EYES

Words by BUDDY BERNIER
Music by JERRY BRAININ

Dm7
G7♭9
Fm
G7♭9
C
Cm
3fr
night has a thou - sand eyes and it
G
D7
G
D7
knows a truth - ful heart from one that lies. Though
G
Am7
D9
4fr
D7
ro - mance may have called in the past my
G
Am7
D7
love for you will be ev - er - last - ing and bright. As

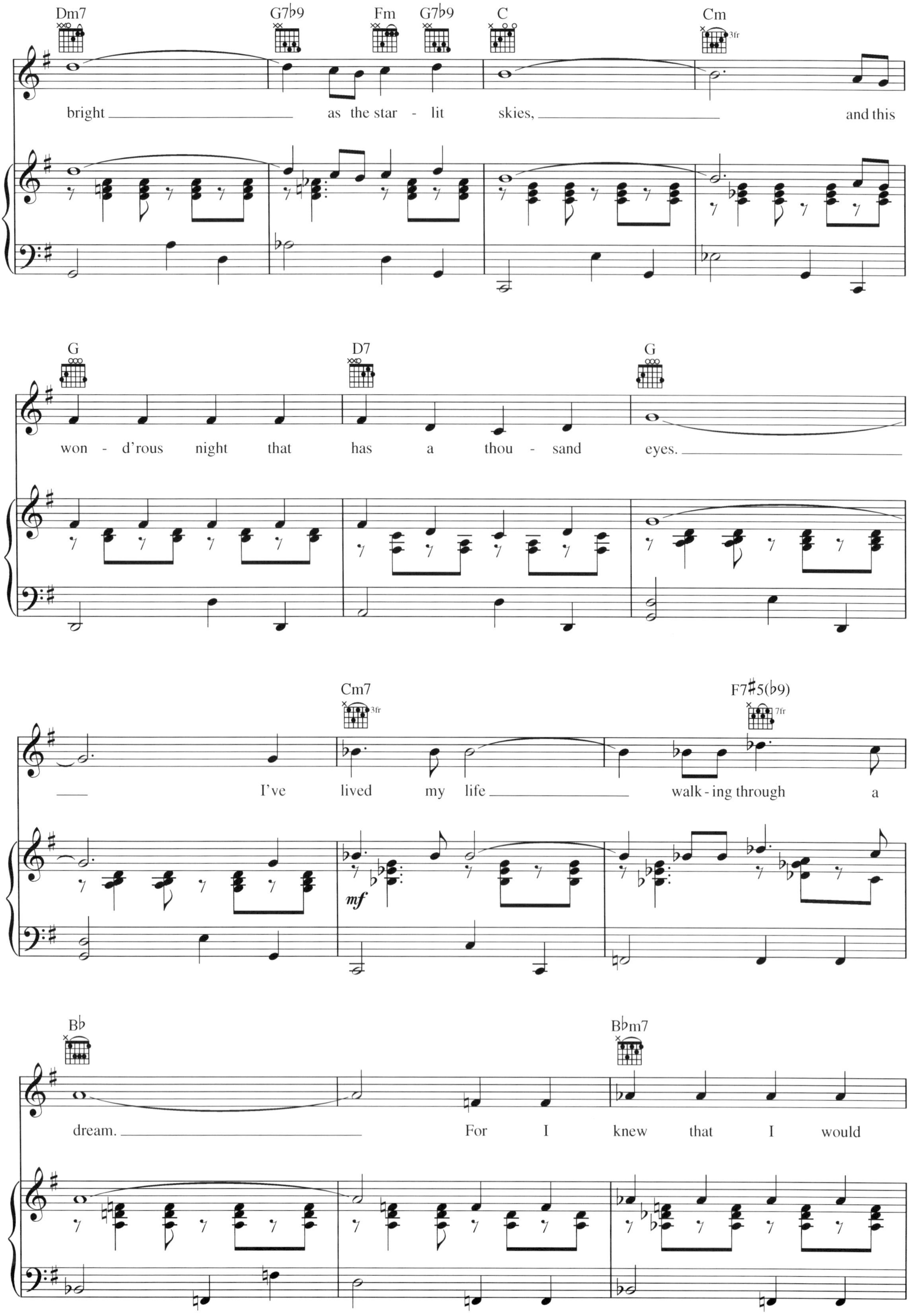
Dm7
G7♭9
Fm
G7♭9
C
Cm
3fr
bright as the star - lit skies, and this
G
D7
G
won - d'rous night that has a thou - sand eyes.
Cm7
3fr
F7♯5(♭9)
7fr
I've lived my life walk - ing through a
mf
B♭
B♭m7
dream. For I knew that I would

E♭7♯5(♭9)
5fr
A♭
4fr
find this mo - ment su - preme. A
F9
G
night of bliss and ten - der sighs and the
mp
Am7
D7
D9
4fr
D7
G
smil - ing down of a thou - sand eyes. The
Fm
D7
D9
4fr
D7
G
night has a thou - sand eyes.

A NIGHT IN TUNISIA

By JOHN "DIZZY" GILLESPIE
and FRANK PAPARELLI

Cm6
3fr
A7♭9
5fr
Dm(maj7)
E♭7
Dm(maj7)
E♭7
Dm(maj7)
E♭7
Dm(maj7)
Gm6
3fr
A7♭9
5fr
Dm(maj7)
Adim
D7♭9
4fr
Gm6
3fr

D7♭9
4fr
Gm(maj7)
3fr
Gm6
3fr
B♭m6
6fr
C7♭9
3
Fmaj7
Fm7
3
3
Edim
3fr
A7♭9
5fr
3
E♭7
3
Dm(maj7)
E♭7
3
Dm(maj7)
E♭7
3
Dm(maj7)

Gm6
3fr
A7♭9
5fr
Dm(maj7)
Dm6
Em7
3
E♭7
Dm7
G9♭5
Gm(maj7)
3fr
Gm7
F♯7♯9
3fr

F6/9 N.C.

B♭m9 E♭9♯11 Dm(maj7) Dm6 E♭9♯11 E♭7 Dm6/9

E♭9♯11 Dm6/9 Fm7

Em7 A7♭9 Dm(maj7) B♭m7 E♭7 B♭m9 E♭9 Dm6/9

B♭m9
6fr
E♭9
Dm6
3
B♭m9
6fr
E♭9♯11
5fr
Dm(maj7)
Gm6
3fr
A7♭9
5fr
Dm(maj7)
Adim
D9
4fr
D7♭9
4fr
Gm6
3fr
D7♭9
4fr
Gm6
3fr
Gm(maj7)
3fr
B♭m6
6fr
D13
4fr
D♭13
3fr

C9
G♭13
F6/9
Edim
A7♭9
B♭m7
E♭9♯11
Dm(maj7)
E♭9
E♭9♯11
Dm6/9
E♭9♯11
Dm6/9
E♭9♯11
Edim
A7♭9
Dm6/9
Dm(maj7)

OH! LOOK AT ME NOW

Words by JOHN DeVRIES
Music by JOE BUSHKIN

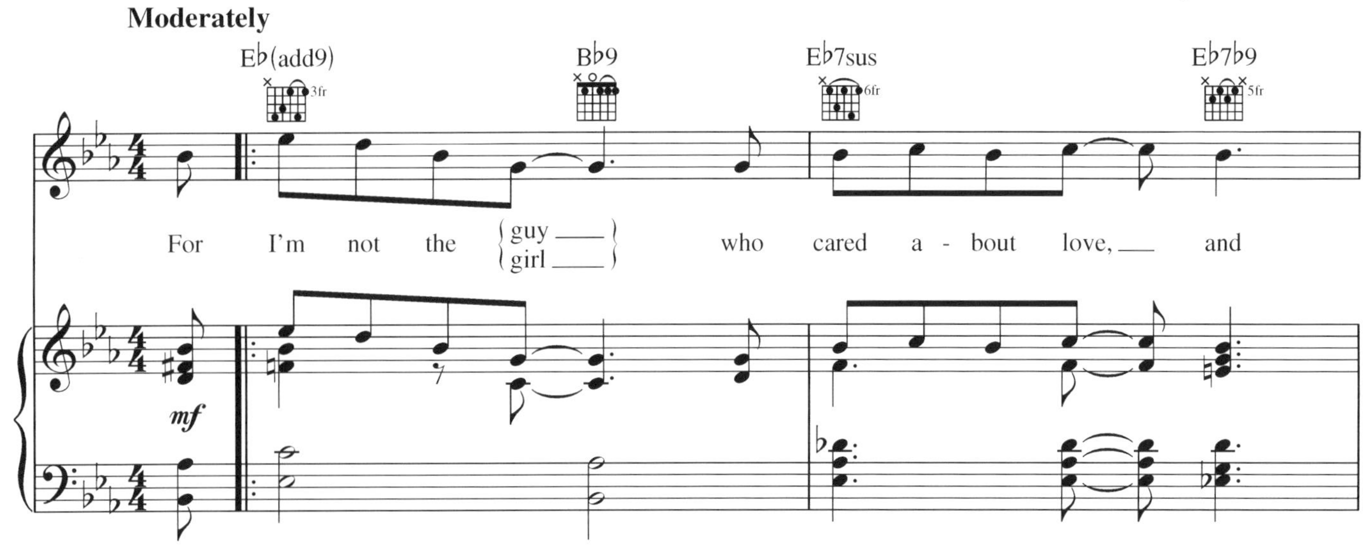

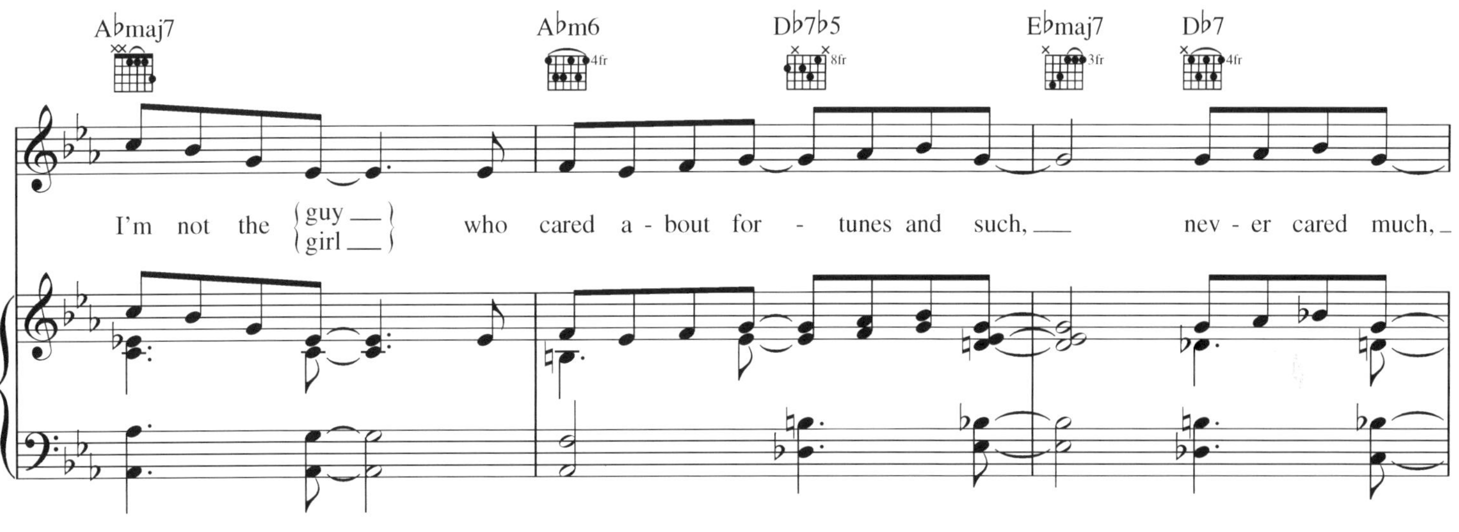

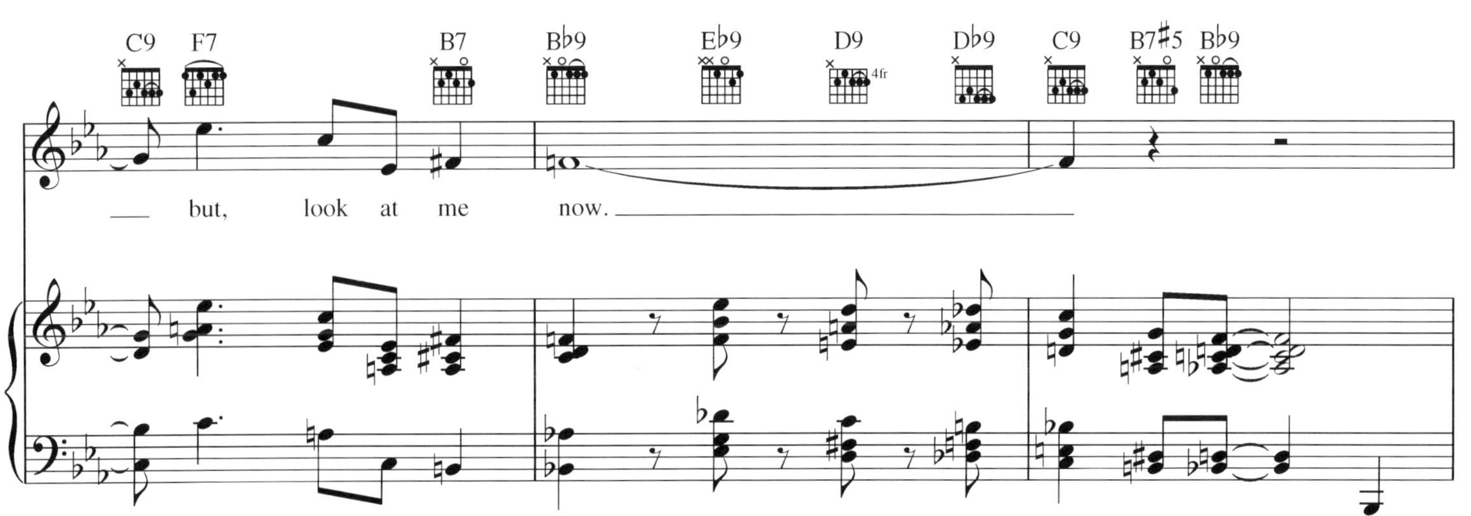

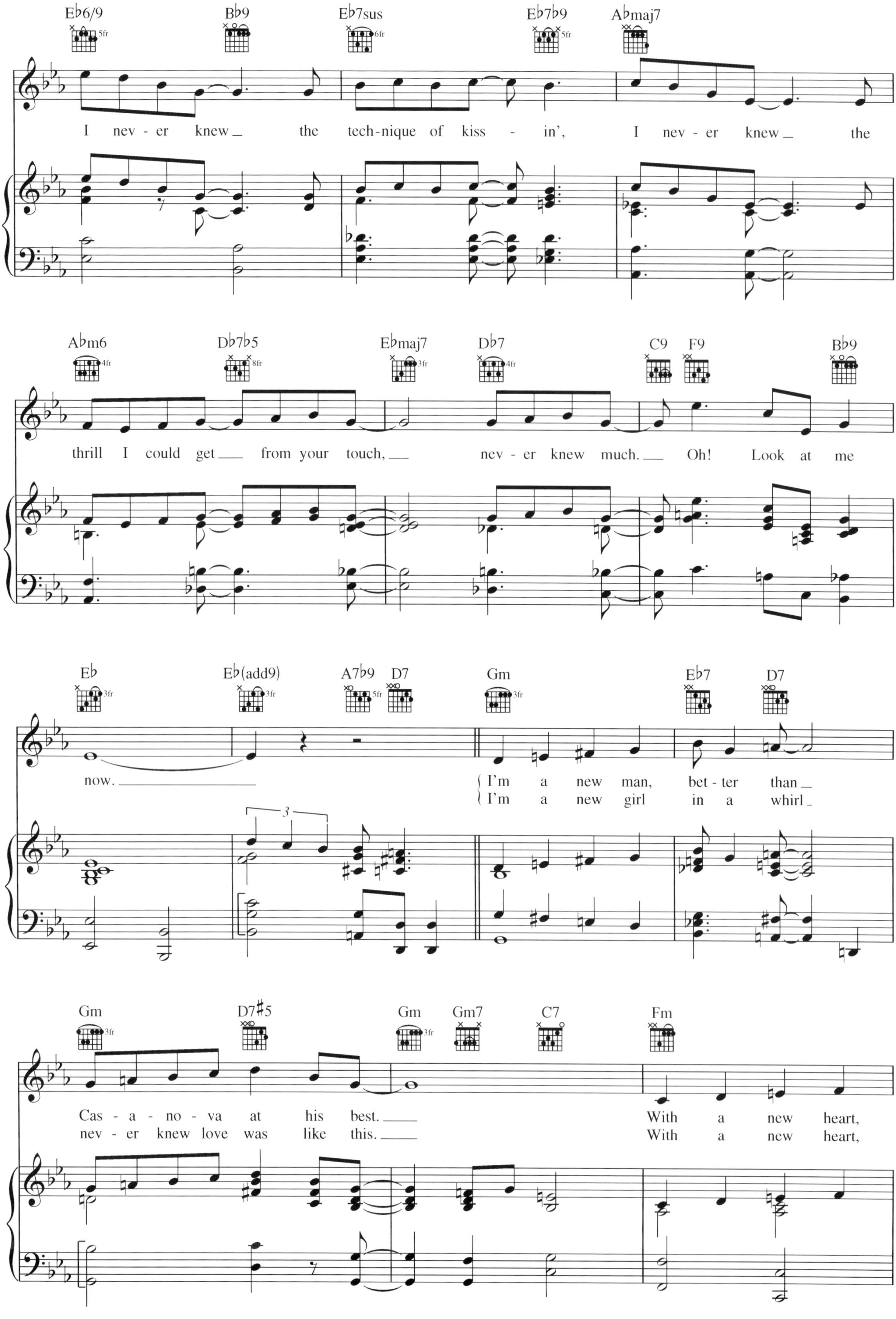

E♭6/9 B♭9 E♭7sus E♭7♭9 A♭maj7

I never knew the technique of kissin', I never knew the

A♭m6 D♭7♭5 E♭maj7 D♭7 C9 F9 B♭9

thrill I could get from your touch, never knew much. Oh! Look at me

E♭ E♭(add9) A7♭9 D7 Gm E♭7 D7

now.
I'm a new man, better than
I'm a new girl in a whirl

Gm D7♯5 Gm Gm7 C7 Fm

Casanova at his best. With a new heart,
never knew love was like this. With a new heart,

D♭7
C7
Fm
Fm7
B♭7
B♭7♯5
brand-new start. I'm so proud I'm bust - in' my vest.
brand-new start. Gon - na be a Mrs., not Miss.
So,
E♭6/9
B♭9
E♭7sus
E♭7♭9
A♭maj7
I am the guy girl who turned out a lov - er.
So, I'm the guy girl who
A♭m6
D♭7♭5
E♭maj7
D♭7
C9
F9
B♭9
laughed at those blue dia - mond rings, one of those things. Oh! Look at me
1
E♭6
Fm7
B♭9
B♭7♯5
2
E♭6
now. For now.

NUAGES

By DJANGO REINHARDT
and JACQUES LARUE

G♭13
F7♭9
F7
B♭6
B♭m6
6fr
F6/9
1
D♭9
Gm7♭5
C7
F6
Gm7
G♯dim7
F6
2
D♭9
Gm7♭5
C7
rit.
F6
Gm7♭5
F6/9

ON A SLOW BOAT TO CHINA

By FRANK LOESSER

F♯7
B7
Leave all your { love - lies / lov - ers }
Bm7
F6/9
E6/9
A
weep-ing on the far - a - way shore.
Out on the bri -
F♯7
Bm
Cdim7
A/C♯
- ny, with a moon big and shi - ny,
melt - ing your heart
C♯7
D
Bm7
C♯m7
4fr
F♯7
Bm7
of stone.
I'd love to get

G7 G♯7 A A/G F♯7
4fr
you on a slow boat to Chi - na,
straight 8th's
Bm7 B♭7 A N.C.
all to my - self, a - lone.
A(♭5) A A/C♯ D6 D♯dim7
There is no verse to this song, 'Cause I don't
8va loco 8va loco
A/E Adim/E♭ Bm7/D Bm7 Esus A
want to wait a mo - ment too long.
8va
Solo (improvise)

F♯7
Bm
Cdim7
A/C♯
C♯7
D
Bm7
C♯m7
4fr
F♯7
Bm7
Get you and keep
Cdim7
A/C♯
A
F♯7
you in my arms ev - er - more,
B7
B6
E/B
N.C.
F6/9
C11/E
leave all your love - lies
lov - ers
weep - ing on the far - a - way shore.

N.C.
F13
B♭6
Out on the bri -
G7
Cm7
C♯dim7
- ny, with a moon big and shi - ny,
B♭/D
B♭
D7♭9
E♭maj7
Cm7
Dm7♭5
G7
melt - ing your heart of stone, I'd
8va
Broader Swing
Cm7
A♭7
B♭
B♭/A♭
love to get you on a slow boat to Chi -

G7♯5
C7
F13
B♭
-na,
all to my-self,
all
B♭/A♭
G7
C7
Cm7/F(add9)
the way to Chi-na,
all to my-self,
B7♯9
B♭6
B♭/A♭
B♭/G
Cm7♭5/G♭
N.C.
a-lone.
piano fill
B♭maj7(add6)
6fr
B♭6/9

ONCE I LOVED
(Amor Em Paz)
(Love In Peace)

Music by ANTONIO CARLOS JOBIM
Portuguese Lyrics by VINICIUS DE MORAES
English Lyrics by RAY GILBERT

Bb9#5
Ebmaj7
3fr
Eb6
I cried at the
I know that no
Em7b5
Eb9#11
5fr
1 Dmaj7
thought. I was fool - ish and proud and let you say good - bye.
mat - ter what - ev - er be - falls, I'll nev - er
D7#5
2 Dmaj7
G7
let you go. I will hold you close.
Cmaj7
F13
Bbmaj7
Make you stay.

Portuguese Lyrics

Eu amei, e amei ai de mim muito mais do que devia amar.
E chorei ao sentir que eu iria sofrer e me desesperar.

Foi antão, que da minha infinita triztesa aconteceu você.
Encontrei, em você a razão de viver e de amar em paz
E não sofrer mais. Nunca mais.
Porque o amor é a coisa mais triste quando se desfaz.
O amor é a coisa mais triste quando se desfaz.

ONE NOTE SAMBA
(Samba De Uma Nota So)

Original Lyrics by NEWTON MENDONCA
English Lyrics by ANTONIO CARLOS JOBIM
Music by ANTONIO CARLOS JOBIM

Dm7 D♭7 Cm7 B9♭5 B♭
as I'm bound to be the un - a - void - a - ble con - se - quence of you.
E♭m7 A♭7
There's so man - y peo - ple who can talk and talk and talk and just say
D♭maj7 D♭6 D♭maj7 D♭6 D♭m7
noth - ing, or near - ly noth - ing.
I have used up all the scale I
G♭7 Bmaj7 B6 Cm7♭5 B7♭5 Dm7 D♭7
know, and at the end I've come to noth - ing, or near-ly noth - ing. So I come back to my first

Cm7
B7♭5
F7♯5
Dm7
D♭7
note, as I must come back to you. I will pour in-to that one
G♭maj7
B7♭5
Fm7
E9♭5
note all the love I feel for you. An-y-one who wants the whole
E♭maj9
A♭7
D♭6
C7
show re, mi, fa, sol, la, ti, do, he will find him-self with no
Bmaj7
B♭
1
F7♯5
2
B♭maj13
show. Bet-ter play the note you know. This is

OUT OF NOWHERE

from the Paramount Picture DUDE RANCH

Words by EDWARD HEYMAN
Music by JOHNNY GREEN

Am
E7
Am
E7
Am
E7
If it's clear or rain - ing, there is no ex -
Am
E7
A7
Em7
A7
plain - ing, things just hap - pen and so did
Am7
D9
4fr
G
you.
You came to me
Eb7
from out of no - where.

G
Bm7
E7
You took my heart and found it free.
Bm7
E7
Am
Bm7♭5
E7
Won - der - ful dreams, won - der - ful schemes from
Am
E♭7
no - where, made ev - 'ry hour sweet as a flow - er for
D9
4fr
G
me. If you should go back to you

E♭7
G
no - where,
leav-ing me with
a mem - o -
Bm7
E7
Bm7
E7
Am
Bm7♭5
E7
ry
I'll al - ways wait
for your re - turn out of
Am
Cm
G/B
B♭dim7
Am7
D7
no - where,
hop - ing you'll bring your love to
1
G
G♯dim7
Am7
D7
2
G
Cm
G
me.
me.

PENNIES FROM HEAVEN

from PENNIES FROM HEAVEN

Words by JOHN BURKE
Music by ARTHUR JOHNSTON

G/B
Em/C#
F#7
Bm
Em7♭5
A7
blue; And no one congrat-u-lat-ed a moon that was al-ways
D9
4 fr
D7
G/F
G+/F
C
Am
D+
new. So it was planned that they would van-ish now and then and you must
G
C9
B9
B♭9
A9
A7
F#m
A+
pay be-fore you get them back a-gain. That's what storms were made for
Am
D13
4 fr
D7
G
A7sus
A7
and you should-n't be a-fraid, for ev-'ry time it rains, it rains
mf

C
D7
Am7
D7
G
A7sus
A7
pen-nies from Heav - en.
Don't you know each cloud con - tains
Am7
D7
Am7
D7
G7
G9
pen-nies from Heav - en?
You'll find your for - tune fall - ing
C
E7
A7
all o - ver town
be sure that your um - brel - la
D7
Am
D9
4 fr
G
A7sus
A7
is up - side down.
Trade them for a pack - age of

C
D7
Am7
D7
G
G7♯5
Sun-shine and flow - ers.
If you want the things you love,
C
Am
C
Em
G+
E♭
3 fr
you must have show - ers,
so when you hear it thun - der
G
G9
F9
E9
Am7
A7
D7
don't run un-der a tree.
There'll be pen-nies from Heav-en for you and
1
G
E♭7
D7
me.
2
G
E♭7
G
me.

PICK YOURSELF UP

from SWING TIME

Words by DOROTHY FIELDS
Music by JEROME KERN

F♯maj7
F♯6
G♯dim
3fr
C♯9
F♯maj7
F♯6
My two feet have - n't met yet, but I'll be
C♯7/E♯
F♯
C7/G
C7
teach - er's pet yet, 'cause I'm gon - na learn to dance or
F
C7sus
C7
F
burst.
poco accel.
Em7♭5
C7
Burthen Polka tempo
Gm7
C7
She: Noth - ing's im - pos - si - ble

Fmaj7 B♭ Em7♭5 A7 Dm7 G7
I have found, for when my chin is on the ground, I
Gm7 C7 Gm7 C7 Gm7 C7
pick my - self up, dust my - self off, start all o - ver a -
F Am D7 Gmaj7 G7
gain. Don't lose your con - fi - dence if you slip, be
3
C6 B7 Em7♭5 A7 Am7 D7
grate - ful for a pleas - ant trip, and pick your - self up,

Am
D7
Am
D7
G
dust your - self off, start all o - ver a - gain.
A♭
4fr
Work like a soul in - spir - ed, till the
bat - tle of the day is won.
C
You may be sick and
tir - ed, but you'll be a man, my son!
C7

Gm
3fr
C7
Fmaj7
B♭
Em7♭5
A7
Will you re - mem - ber the fa - mous men, who had to fall to
Gm7
C7
Gm7
C7
(He breathes audibly)
rise a - gain? So take a deep breath,
Gm7
C7
Gm7
C7
Gm7
C7
pick your - self up, dust your - self off,
Gm7
C7
Gm7
C7
F
start all o - ver a - gain.

POLKA DOTS AND MOONBEAMS

Words by JOHNNY BURKE
Music by JIMMY VAN HEUSEN

Gm7 C7 C9 F Dm Gm7 A+ A7
I the per-plexed one, I held my breath and said, "May I have the next one?"
Dm B♭m F A♭m 4fr Gm7 C9
In my fright-ened arms, pol-ka dots and moon-beams spar-kled on a pug-nosed dream.
F E7 A Gdim Bm7 E7
There were ques-tions in the eyes of oth-er danc-ers
A C♯m7 F♯m Bm7 E7 A Gdim
as we float-ed o-ver the floor. There were ques-tions but my
3

Bm7 Dm E7 F♯m7 Cdim Gm7 C9 E
heart knew all the an - swers and per - haps a few things more.
F Dm Gm7 C9 F Dm
Now in a cot - tage built of li - lacs and laugh - ter I know the mean - ing of the
Gm7 A+ A7 Dm B♭m F Cm
words "ev - er af - ter." And I'll al - ways see pol - ka dots and moon - beams
Gm7 C9 1 F C9 2 F E♭ F
when I kiss the pug - nosed dream.

PRELUDE TO A KISS

Words by IRVING GORDON and IRVING MILLS
Music by DUKE ELLINGTON

Dm7
G7♯5(♭9)
C6
A7♯5(♭9)
D9
4fr
G9♯5
3fr
my pre - lude to a kiss.
If you hear a
C9
Fmaj7
B7♭9
E7
A7♭9
6fr
Dm
song that grows from my ten - der sen - ti - men - tal woes,
Dm7
G7♯5
C6
D13
4fr
Dm7
G7♯5
C6
that was my heart try - ing to com - pose a pre-lude to a kiss.
Emaj7
C♯m7
4fr
F♯m7
B7
Emaj7
C♯m7
4fr
Though it's just a sim - ple mel - o - dy with noth - ing fan - cy,

F♯m7 B7 Emaj7 C♯m7 F♯m7 B7 E Edim7 D9

nothing much, you could turn it to a sym-pho-ny, a Schu-bert tune with a

G7sus E♭7sus D7sus E9♯11 A7♯5(♭9) D9 G9♯5 C9 Fmaj7

Gersh - win touch. Oh! How my love song gen - tly cries for the

B7♭9 E7 A7♭9 Dm Dm7 G7♯5 C6 D13

ten - der - ness with - in your eyes. My love is a pre - lude that nev - er dies,

Dm7 G7♯5(♭9) 1 C Fmaj7 E9♯11 A7♯5 2 C

a pre - lude to a kiss.

SATIN DOLL
from SOPHISTICATED LADIES

Words by JOHNNY MERCER and BILLY STRAYHORN
Music by DUKE ELLINGTON

Dm7
G7
Dm7
G7
Em7
A7
Ba - by, shall we go out skip - pin'? Care - ful, a - mi - go,
Em7
A7
Cm/E♭
D7
A♭m7
D♭7♭9
C6
you're flip - pin'. Speaks Lat - in, that sat - in doll.
Gm7
C7
Gm7
C7
Fmaj7
She's no - bod - y's fool, so I'm play - ing it cool as can be.
G♭maj7
Gmaj7
A♭maj7
Am7
D7
I'll give it a whirl, but I

Am7
D7
G7
Dm7
G7♭9
ain't for no girl catch-ing me.
(Spoken:)
Switch - er - oo - ney.
Dm7
G7
Dm7
G7
Em7
A7
Tel - e-phone num - bers well you know, do - ing my rhum - bas
Em7
A7
Cm/E♭
D7
A♭m7
D♭7♭9
C6
3fr
4fr
with u - no, and that 'n', my sat - in doll.
1
2

QUIET NIGHTS OF QUIET STARS
(Corcovado)

English Words by GENE LEES
Original Words & Music by ANTONIO CARLOS JOBIM

D9/A
4fr
A♭dim7
Qui - et nights of qui - et stars,
qui - et chords from my
Gm7
G♭7
gui - tar
float - ing on the si - lence that sur - rounds
Fmaj7
F6
Fmaj7
Gm7
Am7
Fmaj7
Fm7
us.
Qui - et thoughts and qui -
Em7
A7♯5
- et dreams,
qui - et walks by qui - et streams,

D9
4fr
Dm7
A♭dim7
and a win - dow look - ing on the moun - tains and the sea.
D9/A
4fr
How love - ly! This is where I want to be.
A♭dim7
Gm7
Here, with you so close to me, un - til the fi - nal
3
G♭7
Fmaj7
F6
Fmaj7
Gm7
Am7
Gm7
flick - er of life's em - ber.

Fm7
Fm(maj7)
Fm6
Em7
I, who was lost and lone - ly, be - liev - ing life was
Am7
Dm7
G7♭9
Em7
on - ly a bit - ter, trag - ic joke, have found with you
A7♯5
Dm7
G9
9fr
G7♭9
the mean - ing of ex - ist - ence. Oh, my love.
1
C6
B♭9
A7♯5
2
C6
B♭9
D♭7
4fr
C6/9
rit.

RUBY, MY DEAR

By THELONIOUS MONK

Bb6/9
Bdim7
Cm7
Dm9
Ebm7
Ab9#11
A9#11
Fm9
Bb7b9
Ebmaj9
Fm7
F#dim7
Gm9
C9
Fmaj9
Gm7
Am7
Bbm9
Eb7b9
Abmaj9
To Coda
Bbm11
A7
Bm11
Bb7#11
D.S. al Coda
CODA
Bbm11
A7
Gb9
G7b9
Abmaj7#11
8va
15ma
8va
15ma

SMALL FRY

from the Paramount Picture SING, YOU SINNERS

Words by FRANK LOESSER
Music by HOAGY CARMICHAEL

D
E9
A7
Just watch me teach him with the sole of my shoe.
D
B7
E7
G7
A7
D
B7
Small fry, strut-tin' by the pool-room; small fry
E7
G7
A7
D
D7(add13)
4fr
should be in the school - room. My! My! Put
G9
9fr
B7/F♯
E7
down that cig - a - rette; you ain't a grown - up high and might - y

A7sus
A7
D
B7
E7
G7
A7
yet.
Small fry, dance - in' for a pen - ny;
small fry, you kissed the neigh-bor's daugh-ter;
D
B7
E7
G7
A7
small fry, count - in' up how man - y.
small fry should stay in shal - low wa - ter.
D
D7(add13)
G9
B7/F♯
My! My! Just lis - ten here to me, you
Seems I should take you 'cross my knee; you
E7
G
Em7
D
G/D
D
D7(add13)
ain't the big - gest cat - fish in the sea. You prac - tice
ain't the big - gest cat - fish in the sea. You've got your

G9
D/A
F♯7
Bm
A
G
peck - in' all day long to some old ra - di - o song. Oh! yes,
feet all soak - in' wet, you'll be the death of me yet. Oh! me,
A7
D
G/D
D
D7(add13)
Oh! yes, Oh! yes. You bet - ter
Oh! my, small fry.
lis - ten to your maw paw and some - day prac - tice the law, and then you'll
E7
A7sus
A9♯5
be a real suc - cess. Yes,
rit.

SO NICE
(Summer Samba)

Original Words and Music by MARCOS VALLE
and PAULO SERGIO VALLE
English Words by NORMAN GIMBEL

D7♭9
Gm7
Em7♭5
A7♯5
life would be so nice if one day I'd
Dm
Dm7
G13
Gm7
find some-one who would take my hand and sam-ba through life
D♭9
C9
F
with me. Some-one to cling to me, stay with me right or wrong,
Bm7
E7
B♭maj7
some-one to sing to me some lit-tle sam-ba song. Some-one to take my heart,

B♭6
E♭9
then give his heart to me. Some-one who's read-y to give love a start with me.
Am7
D7♭9
4fr
Gm7
Oh yes, that would be so nice.
C7♭9
F
B♭9
Should it be you and me, I could see it would be
1
F6
Gm7
C7♭9
nice.
2
F6
E♭9
G♭maj7
Fmaj9
nice.

SOME OTHER SPRING

Words and Music by ARTHUR HERZOG, JR.
and IRENE KITCHINGS

Gm6
Gdim
Dm
Fm6
A♭7
G7
twi - light falls, __ will the night bring __ a - noth - er to me?
C7
B+
B♭9
E♭
Gm
Fm7
Bdim
Not your kind, but let me find __ it's not true that
E♭
E♭9
D7
D6
D♭6
C6
D9
love is blind! __ Sun - shine's a - round me, but
G7
Gdim
Am7
D7
Em7
A7♯5
deep in my heart it's cold as ice. __ Love, once you

D
C7
B
A♭9
A6
A9
D7
G7♯5
found me, but can that sto - ry un - fold twice?
C
G7♯5
Gm6
Gdim
Dm
Fm6
Some oth - er spring, will my heart wake? Stir - ring to sing love's
A♭7
G7
C7
B+
B♭9
Cm6
A♭9
mag - ic mu - sic? Then for - get the old du - et find
C
D9
Fdim
1
C
G7♯5
2
C
love in some oth - er spring?
spring?

SOME DAY MY PRINCE WILL COME

Words by LARRY MOREY
Music by FRANK CHURCHILL

Gm7 C7 F A+ B♭dim
me. He'll whis - per "I love
beat. Some - day we'll say and
D7 Gm B♭+/F♯ C7
you" And steal a kiss or two. Though he's
do things we've been long - ing to. Though she's
F A7 A+ B♭+ Bdim F Adim
far a - way I'll find my love some - day, some - day when my
Gm7 C7 F A♭7 Gm7 C7 F
1
2
dreams come true. true.
8vb

THE SONG IS YOU

Lyrics by OSCAR HAMMERSTEIN II
Music by JEROME KERN

Cmaj9
G9
9fr
C
Cdim
3fr
start, then melt a - way.
I hear mu - sic when I touch your
Dm7
G7
C
C♯dim7
hand, a beau - ti - ful mel - o - dy from some en - chant - ed
G7
Cmaj7
A7♯5
land. Down deep in my heart, I hear it
Dm
G9
9fr
C
say, "Is this the day?"

E
Emaj7
A/C♯
Dm
B9/D♯
6fr
I a - lone have heard this lone - ly strain,
Emaj7
D♯7
I a - lone have heard this glad re - frain.
G♯m
4fr
C♯9
Must it be for - ev - er in - side of me? Why can't I
3
F♯13
B13
7fr
let it go? Why can't I let you know? Why can't I
cresc.
poco rit.

C/G
Cdim/G
G7
let you know the song my heart would sing, that beau - ti - ful
C
C9
F
Fm6
rhap - so - dy of love and youth and spring? The mu - sic is
Cmaj7/E
A7♯5
Dm
G9
sweet, the words are true, the song is
C
you.

SOPHISTICATED LADY

from SOPHISTICATED LADIES

Words and Music by DUKE ELLINGTON,
IRVING MILLS and MITCHELL PARISH

B♭m7
G♭7
F7
E7
E♭7
A♭maj7
Then, with dis - il - lu - sion deep in your eyes, you learned that
A♭7
G7
G♭7
F7
B♭7
E♭7
fools in love soon grow wise. The years have changed you, some - how; I
A♭
Am7♭5
D7
G
Em
see you now... Smok - ing, drink - ing, nev -
Am
D7
G
G♯dim7
Am7
D7♯5
- er think - ing of to - mor - row, non - cha - lant.

G
Em
Am
D7
G
Bdim7
Cm
Diamonds shining, dancing, dining with some man in a restaurant;
Eb7
D7
Bbm7
Gb7
F7
E7
Eb7
is that all you really want? No, Sophisticated lady, I
Abmaj7
Ab9
G9
Gb9
F9
Bb7
Eb7
know, you miss the love you lost long ago, and when nobody is nigh you
1
Ab
Ddim7
Dbm6
Cm6
Bm6
cry. They
2
Ab
Ab6
cry.

STOLEN MOMENTS

Music by OLIVER NELSON

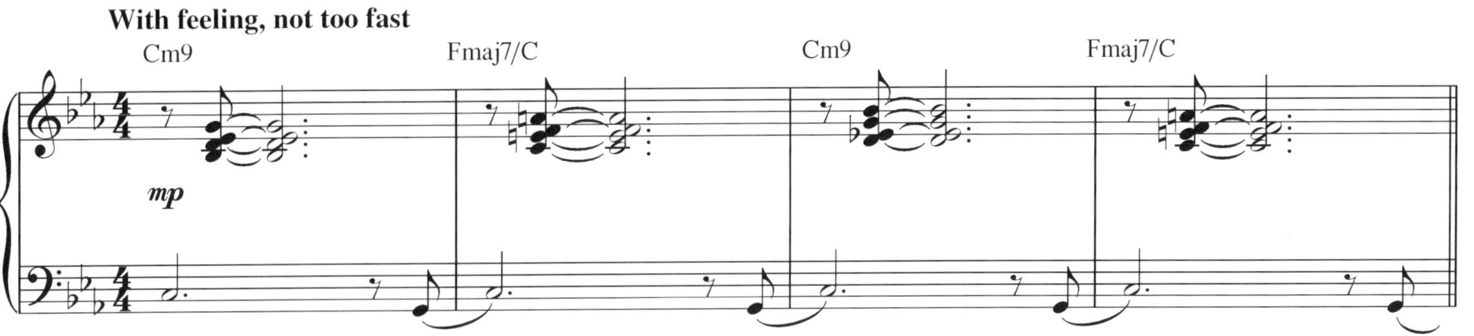

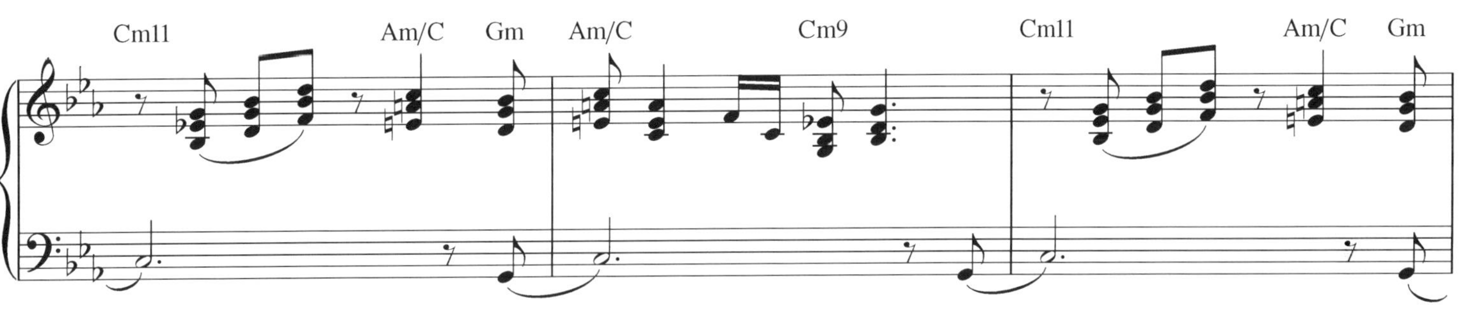

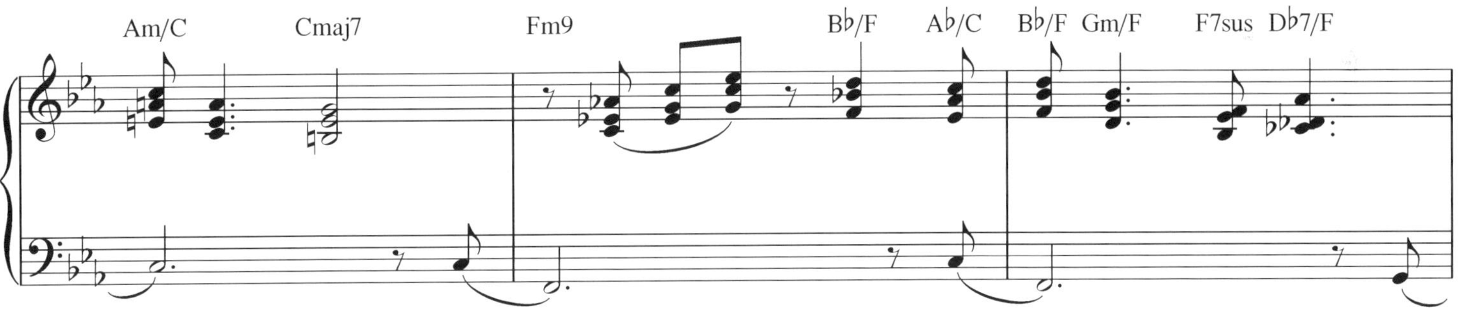

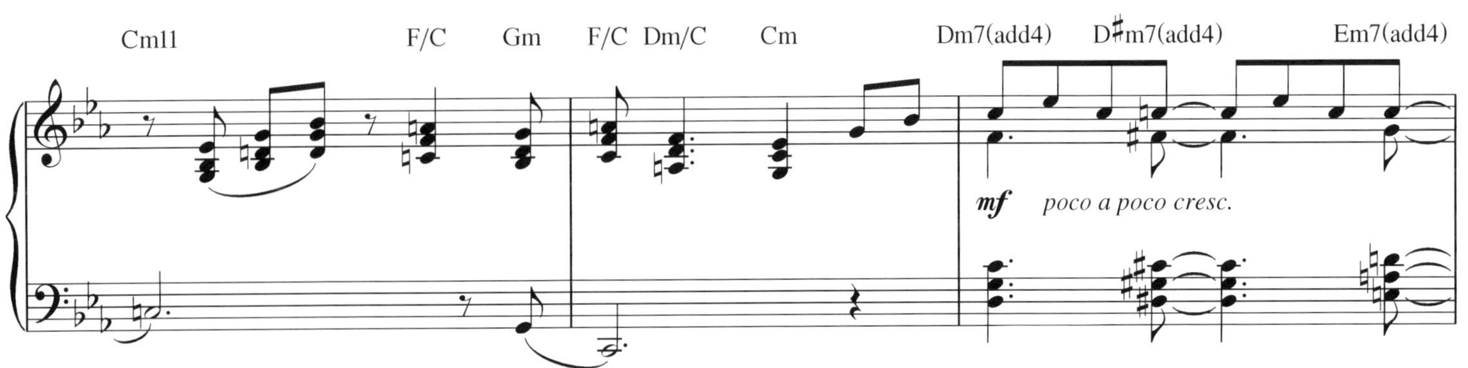

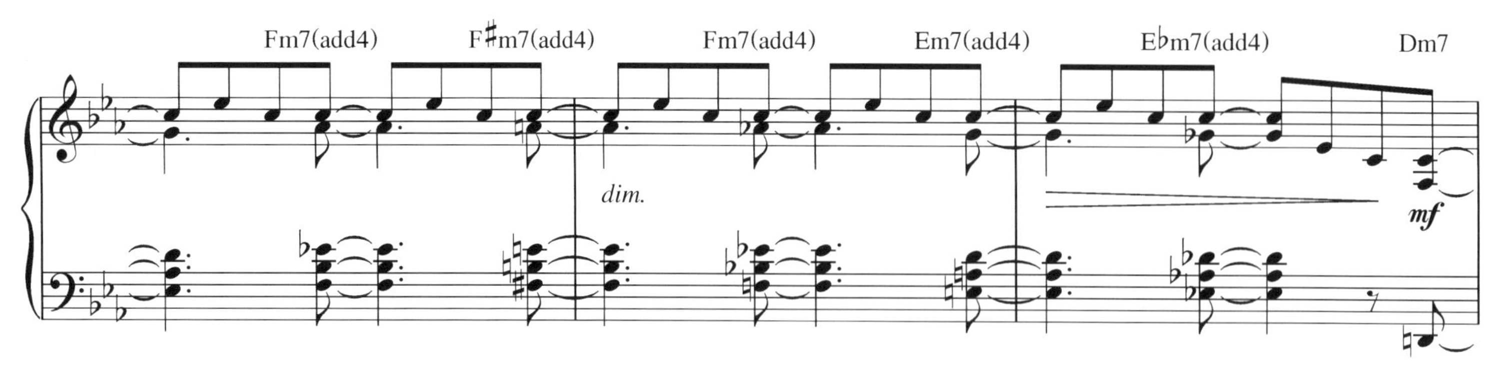
Fm7(add4)
F♯m7(add4)
Fm7(add4)
Em7(add4)
E♭m7(add4)
Dm7
dim.
mf

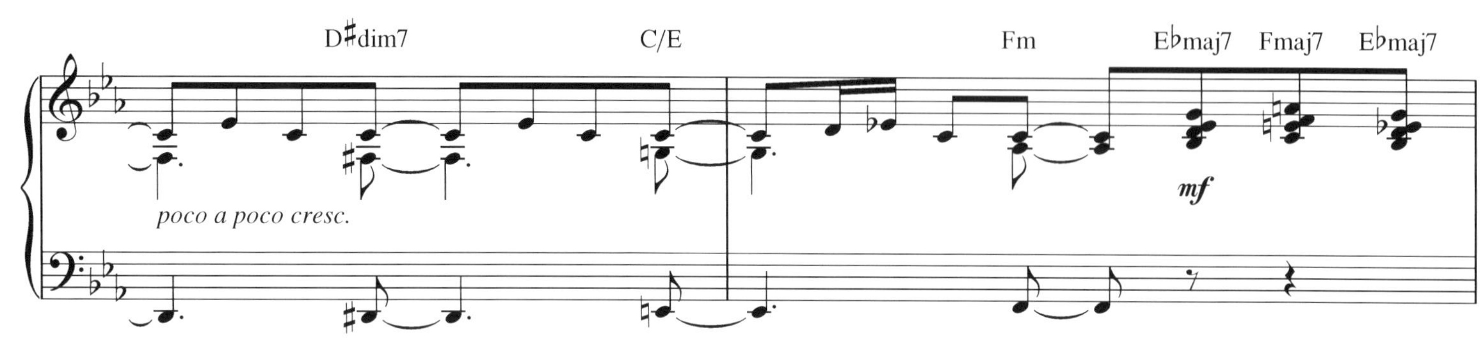
D♯dim7
C/E
Fm
E♭maj7
Fmaj7
E♭maj7
poco a poco cresc.
mf

Fmaj7
E♭maj7
Gsus(add2)
Cm11
Fmaj7/C
E♭maj7/G
mp

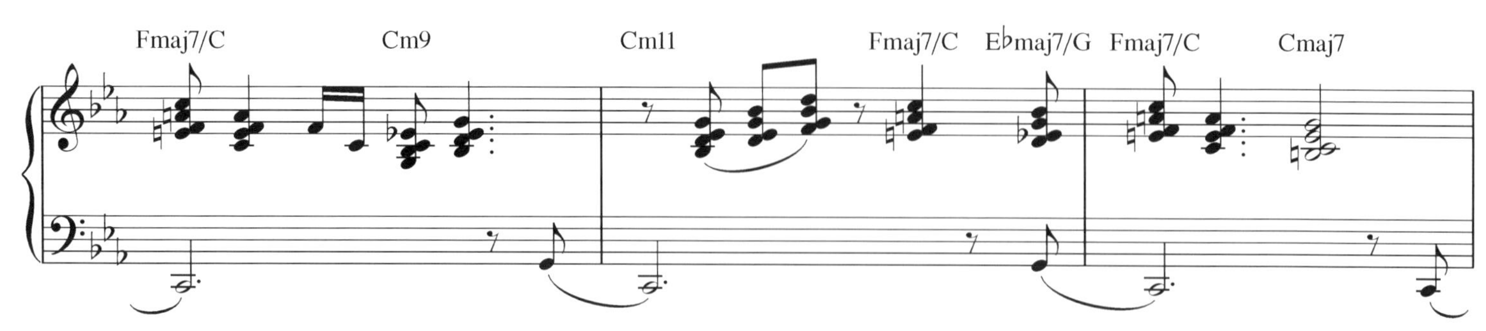
Fmaj7/C
Cm9
Cm11
Fmaj7/C
E♭maj7/G
Fmaj7/C
Cmaj7

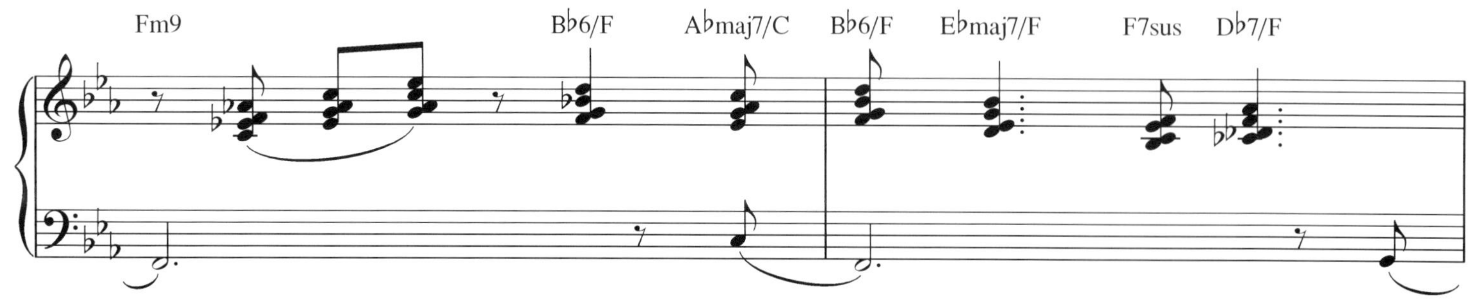
Fm9
B♭6/F
A♭maj7/C
B♭6/F
E♭maj7/F
F7sus
D♭7/F

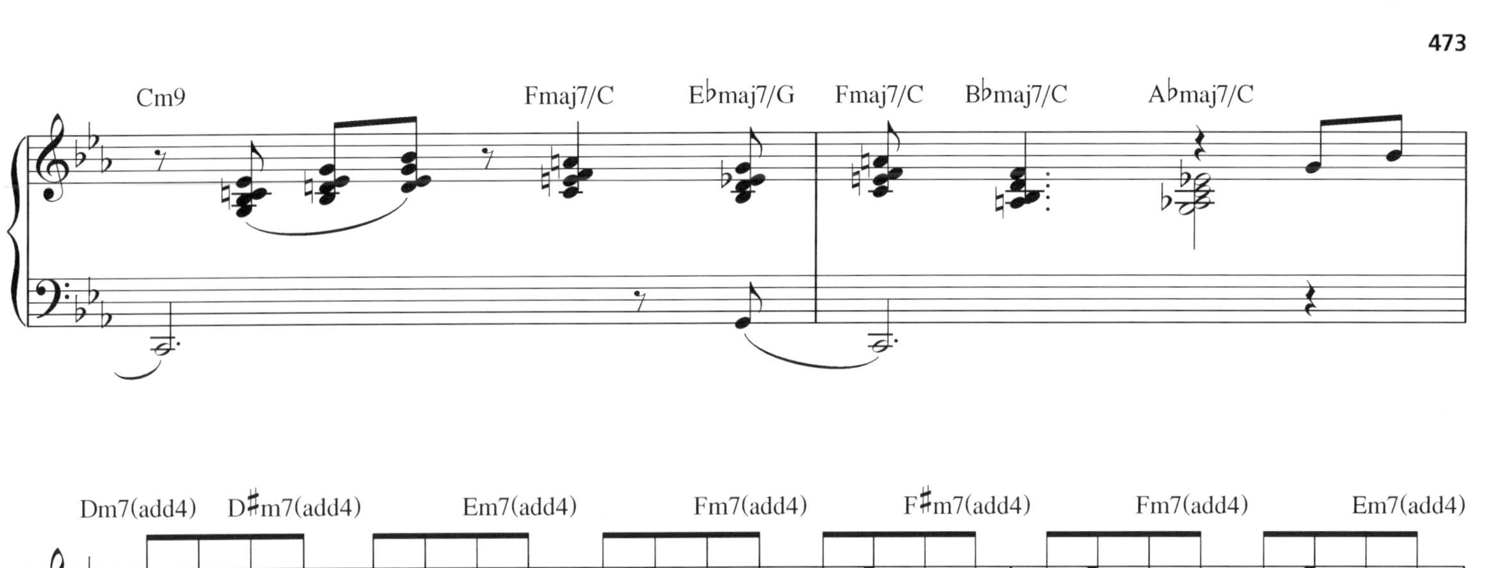
Cm9
Fmaj7/C
E♭maj7/G
Fmaj7/C
B♭maj7/C
A♭maj7/C

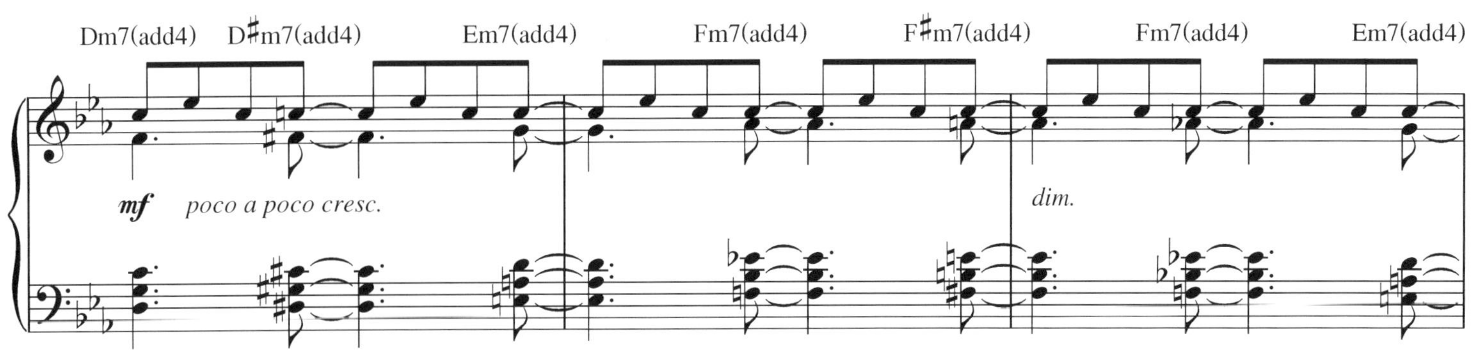
Dm7(add4)
D♯m7(add4)
Em7(add4)
Fm7(add4)
F♯m7(add4)
Fm7(add4)
Em7(add4)
mf
poco a poco cresc.
dim.

E♭m7(add4)
Dm7
D♯dim7
C/E
Fm
E♭maj7
Fmaj7
E♭maj7
mf
poco a poco cresc.
mf

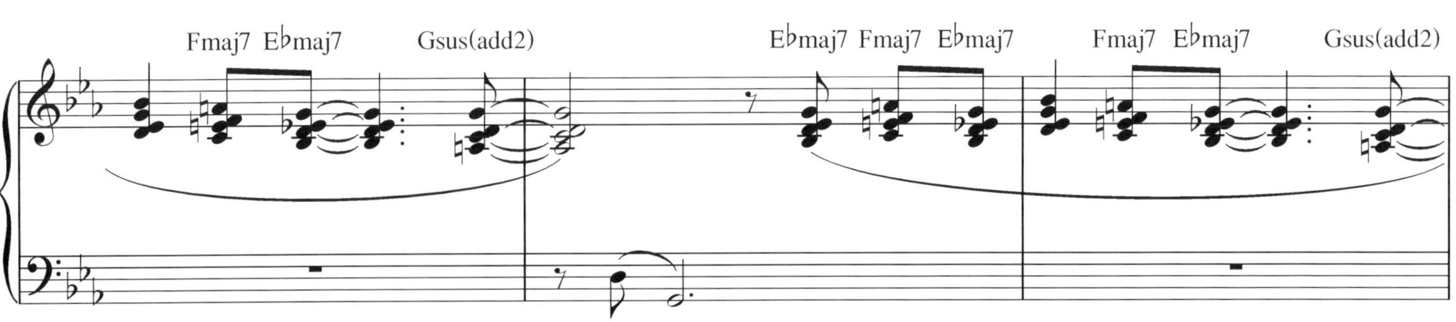
Fmaj7
E♭maj7
Gsus(add2)
E♭maj7
Fmaj7
E♭maj7
Fmaj7
E♭maj7
Gsus(add2)

Cm/G
F9sus
Fm9
Cm13
rit.

STELLA BY STARLIGHT

from the Paramount Picture THE UNINVITED

Words by NED WASHINGTON
Music by VICTOR YOUNG

Moderately slow

F/A Ab dim7 Gm7

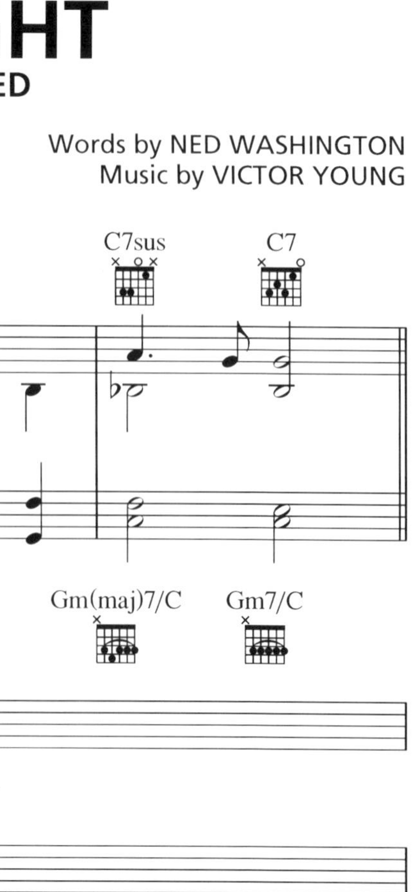

mf

F/C Am/C Gm/C Gm(maj)7/C Gm7/C

Have you seen Stel - la by star - light,

Am G#dim7/A Am7 D9 D7b9

Have you seen Stel - la by star - light,

G/B
E♭7/B♭
Am7
D7
G/D
when have you known rap - ture so rare? The
C♯m7♭5
F♯7
Am7
song a rob - in sings
D7♯5
D7
Dm9/G
G7♭9
through years of end - less
Cmaj9
F13
G/D
springs. The mur - mur of a

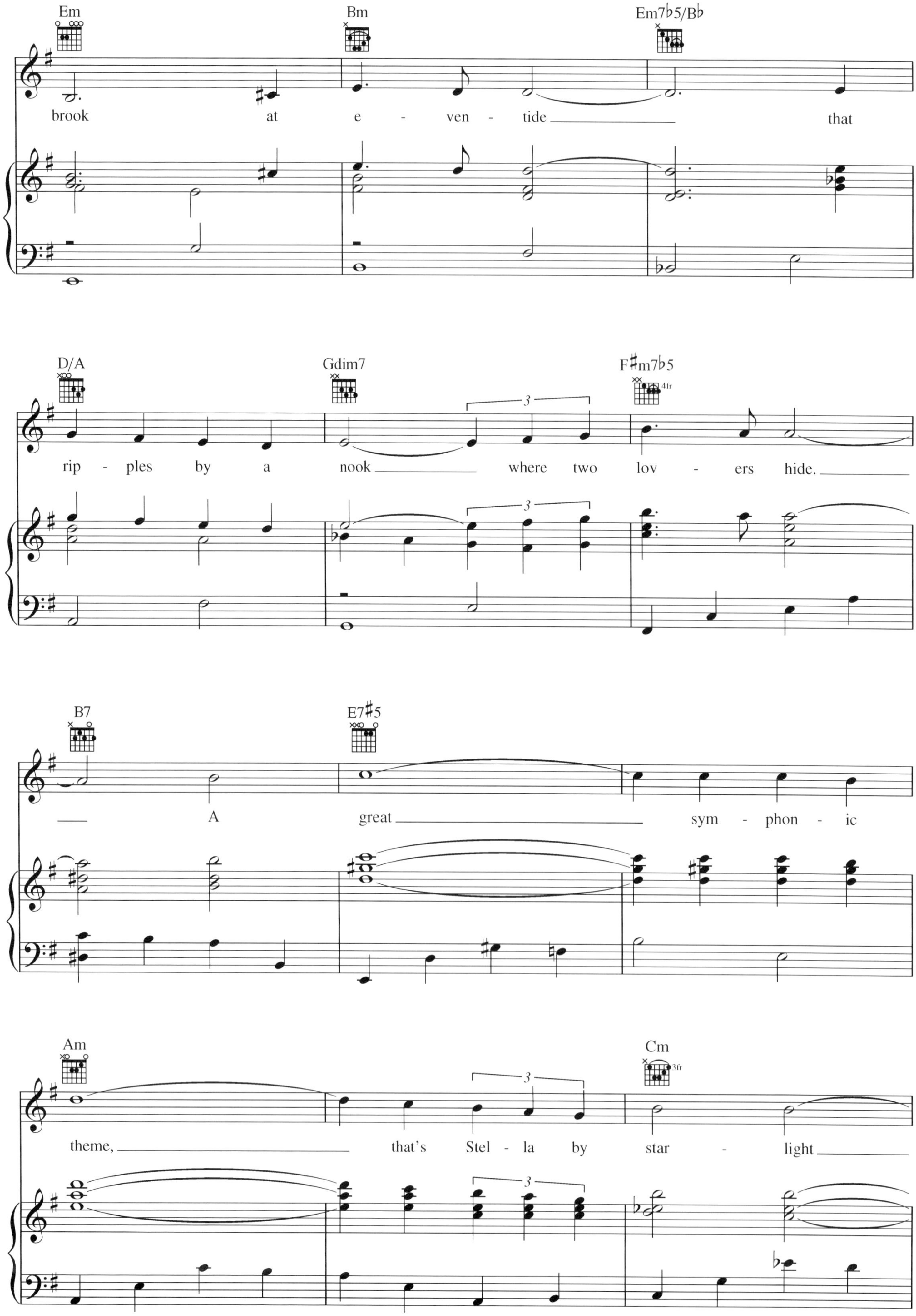

Em Bm Em7♭5/B♭

brook at e - ven - tide ___ that

D/A Gdim7 F♯m7♭5

rip - ples by a nook ___ where two lov - ers hide. ___

B7 E7♯5

___ A great ___ sym - phon - ic

Am Cm

theme, ___ that's Stel - la by star - light ___

G6/9
and not a dream.
Boy: My
Girl: She's
C♯m7♭5
4fr
F♯7
Bm7♭5
heart and I a - gree
all of these and more
E7
Am7♭5
she's ev - 'ry - thing
she's ev - 'ry - thing
D7
G(add9)
on earth to me.
that you'd a - dore.

STOMPIN' AT THE SAVOY

Words and Music by BENNY GOODMAN,
EDGAR SAMPSON, CHICK WEBB and ANDY RAZAF

F
C9
F
just like a cling - in' vine,
Your lips so warm and sweet as wine,
F♯dim7
Gm
C7
Gm
C9
Your cheek so soft and close to mine,
di - vine!
F
F7
B♭7
B7
B♭7
How my heart is sing - in'
E♭9
B♭m7♭5
E♭9
A♭7
A7
While the band is swing - in'!
Nev - er tired of

Ab7
Db7
C7
C9
roam - in' And stomp - in' with you at the Sa - voy. What joy!
F
C9
F
A per - fect hol - i - day! Sa - voy, where we can glide and sway;
F#dim7
Gm
C7
Gm
C9
Sa - voy, there let me stomp a - way with you.
1
F
C9
2
F
Eb9b5
Fmaj9
Sa - voy,

STREET LIFE

Words and Music by WILL JENNINGS
and JOE SAMPLE

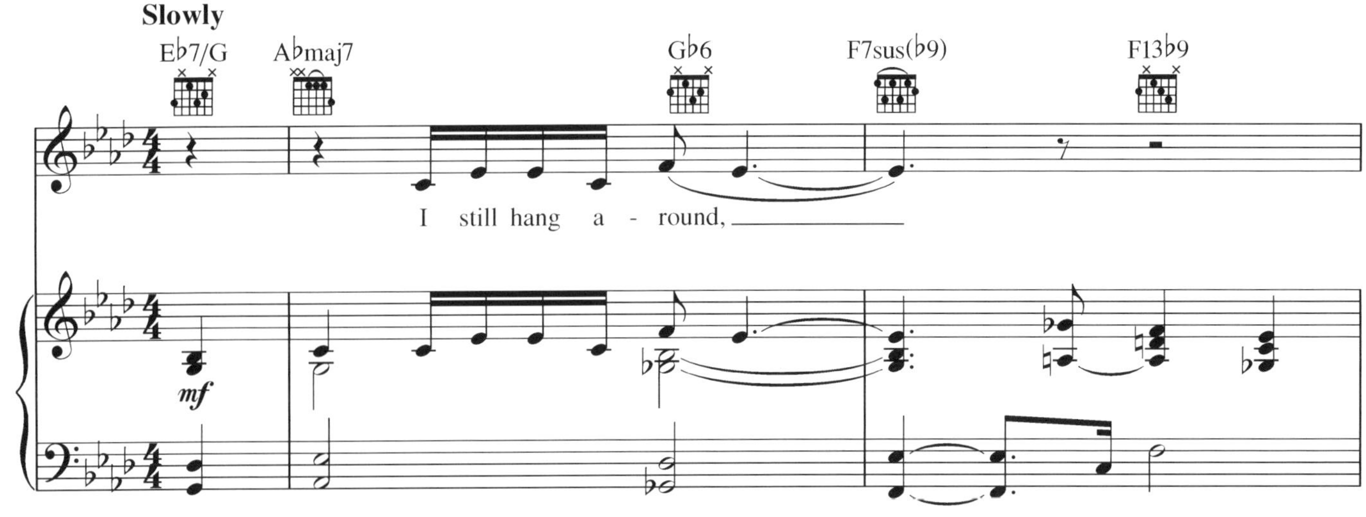

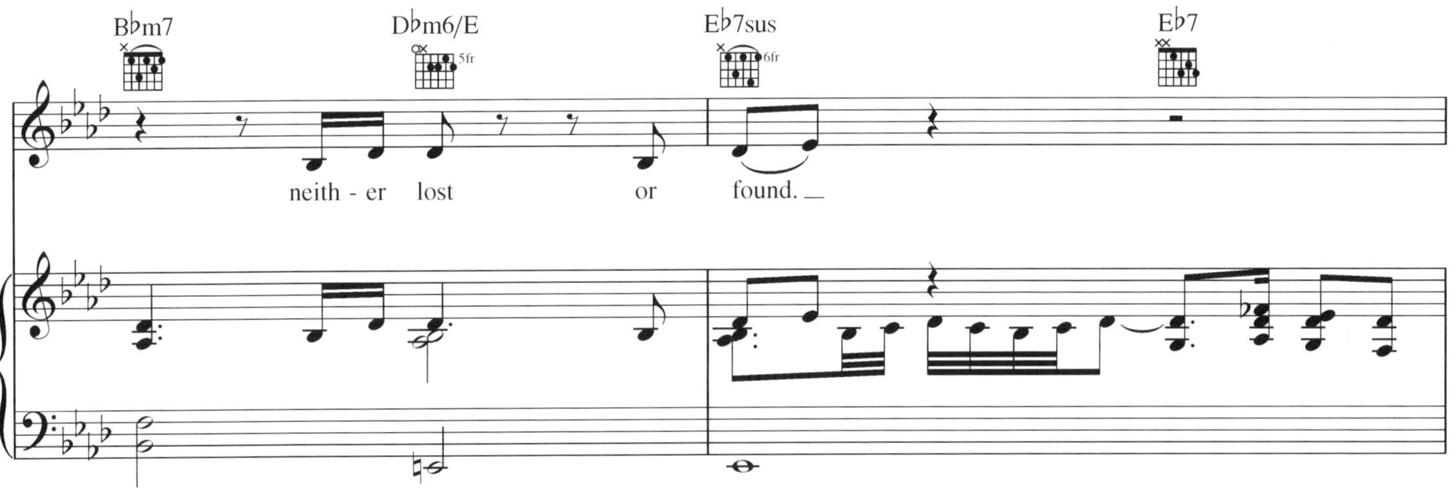

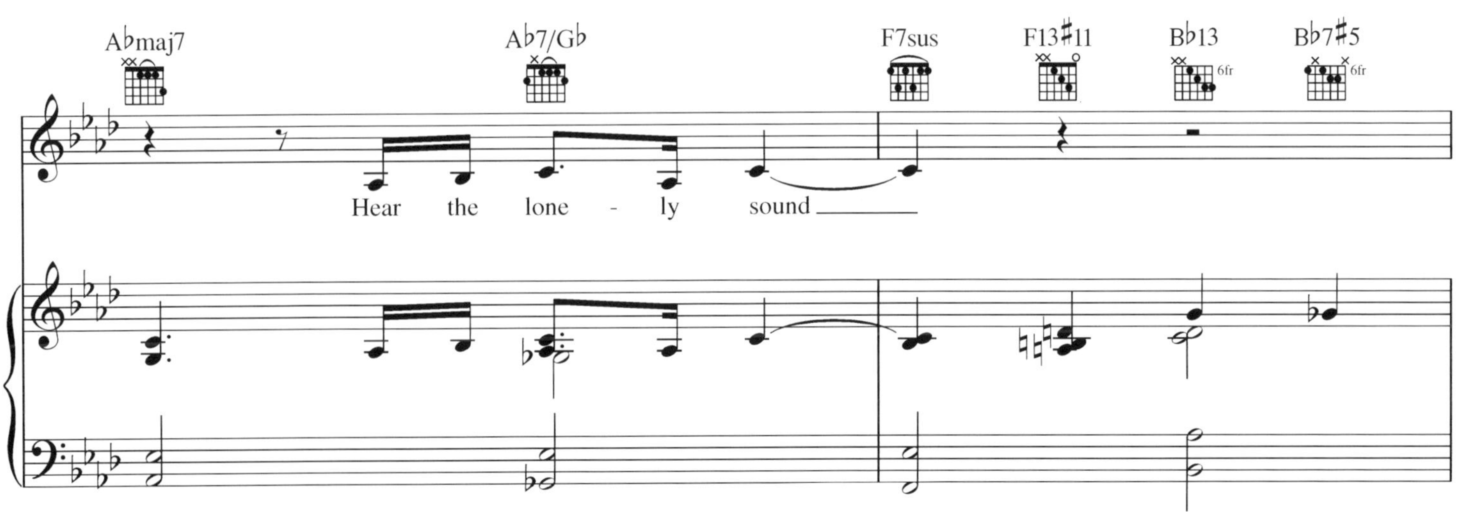

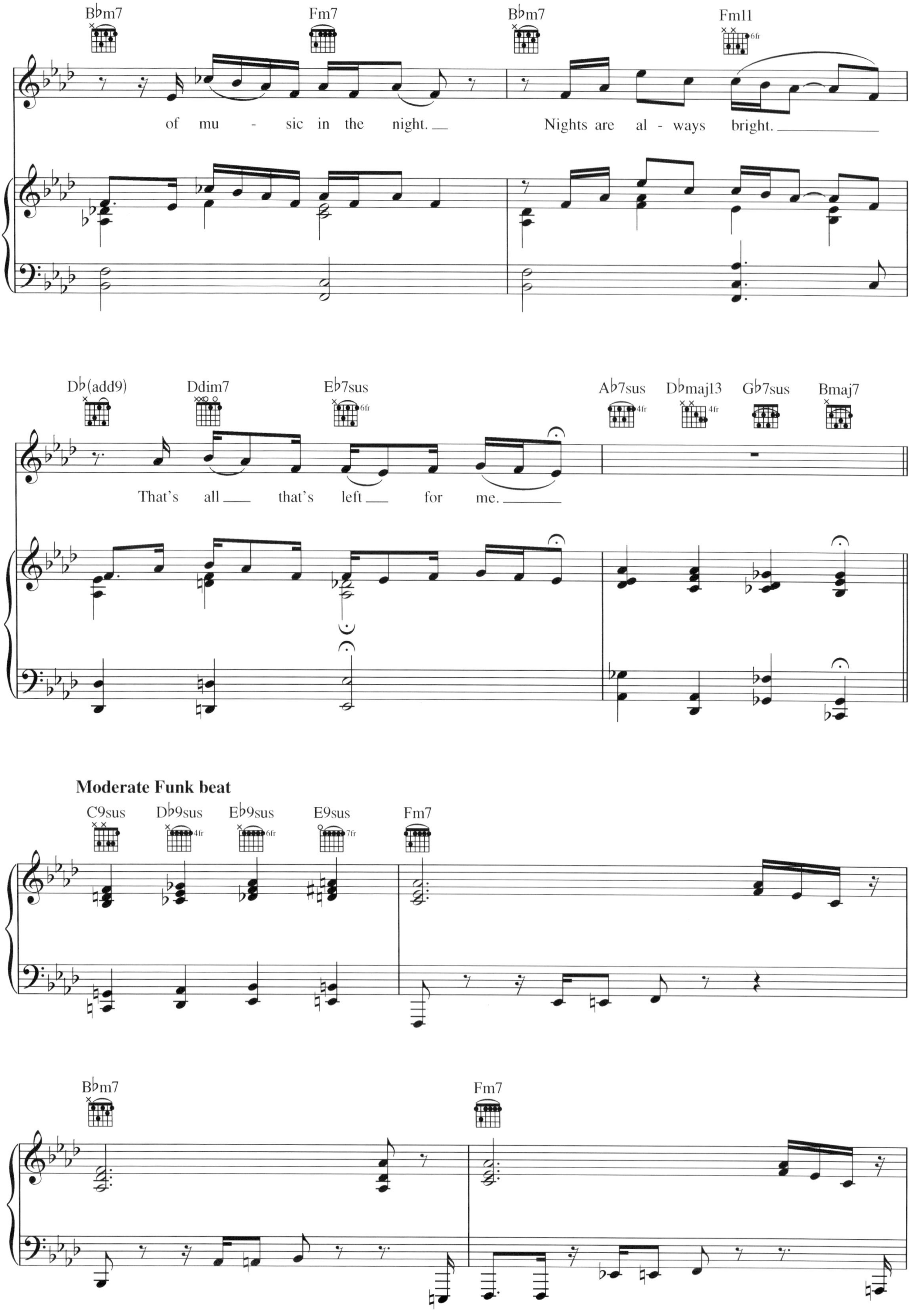
B♭m7
Fm7
B♭m7
Fm11
6fr
of mu - sic in the night.
Nights are al - ways bright.
D♭(add9)
Ddim7
E♭7sus
6fr
A♭7sus
4fr
D♭maj13
4fr
G♭7sus
Bmaj7
That's all that's left for me.
Moderate Funk beat
C9sus
D♭9sus
4fr
E♭9sus
6fr
E9sus
7fr
Fm7
B♭m7
Fm7

B♭m7
Fm7
I play the street - life, be - cause there's no
Street - life, you can run
B♭m11
4fr
Cm11
place I can go. Street - life, it's the on -
a - way from time. Street - life, for a nick -
Fm7
- ly life I know. Street - life, and there's a
- el or a dime. Street - life, but you
B♭m11
4fr
Cm11
thou - sand parts to play. Street - life, un - til you play
bet - ter not get old. Street - life, or you're gon -

Fm7 Bbm7 Eb7sus

your life away. You let the people see just
-na feel the cold. There's always love for sale, a

Cm11 F7#9 Bbm7 Eb7sus

who you wanna be, and ev'ry night you shine just
grown-up fairy tale. Prince Charming always smiles be-

Abmaj7 1 Abm7 Db7sus

like a superstar. That's how the life is played, a
hind a silver spoon, and

Gbmaj7 Gm7b5 Bbm7 Eb7sus

ten-cent masquerade. You dress, you walk, you talk, you're

A♭maj7
C7♯9
2
D♭m7
4fr
G♭7sus
Bmaj7
who you think you are.
if you keep it young, your
Bm7
E7sus
Amaj7
B♭m7
E♭7sus
6fr
song is al - ways sung.
Your love will pay your way, be -
A♭maj7
To Coda
Emaj7
B7/D♯
neath the sil - ver moon.
Street - life.
C♯m9
B7
Emaj7
B7/D♯
C♯m9
B7
Street - life.

Fmaj7 C7/E Dm9 C7 Fmaj7 C7/E

Street - life. Oh, street - life.

Dm7 B♭7sus A♭maj7 B♭7sus 1 A♭maj7 B♭7sus

D.S. al Coda (with repeat)

2 A♭maj7 C9sus D♭9sus E♭9sus E9sus

I play the

CODA

Emaj7 B7/D♯ C♯m9 B7 Emaj7 B7/D♯

Street - life. Street - life.

(Lead vocal ad lib. 2nd time)

C♯m9
B7
Fmaj7
C7/E
Dm9
C7
Street - life.
Oh,
1
2
street - life.
street - life.
Bb7sus
Abmaj7
(Lead vocal ad lib.)
Repeat and Fade
Optional Ending
Ab9♯11
Db13sus
Gbmaj9
Bm(add9)

SUDDENLY IT'S SPRING

from the Paramount Motion Picture LADY IN THE DARK
from the Paramount Motion Picture SUDDENLY IT'S SPRING

Words by JOHNNY BURKE
Music by JAMES VAN HEUSEN

Gm
3fr
F♯dim
9fr
Gm/F
A7/E
Dm/A
A7
D♭dim7/D
5fr
Dm7/A
Why do I keep sigh - ing, not sad, just sigh -
G13
3fr
A♭dim7
A6
A6/C♯
2fr
Bm11
E9
- ing? I'm young and free, and sud - den - ly, it's
A6
Gm11
C13
2fr
E♭9sus/F
6fr
spring. High on a hill -
3
3
F7♭9
B♭6/F
Edim7/F
8fr
F9sus
F7/B♭
B♭6
- top, love is call - ing.

D7sus D7 F♯dim7/G Gm D♭7 C7 Gdim7/F F Am7♭5/E♭ D7
Some - one should wish me "hap - py fall - ing."
Gm F♯dim Gm/F A7/E Dm/A A7 D♭dim7/D Dm7/A
No more be - ing lone - ly. Can I be
G13 A♭dim7 Gm7 C7sus Gm7 C7sus
lone - ly? You look at me, and sud - den - ly, it's
F6 Cm7 Dm7 E♭maj7 F6 C13 Cm7 D7
D.S. al Coda
spring. (Sud - den - ly, it's spring.)

CODA
Gm
F♯dim
Gm/F
A7/E
Dm/A
A7
No more being lonely.
D♭dim7/D
Dm7/A
G13
A♭dim7
Can I be lonely? You
Gm11
C7
look at me, and suddenly,
G♭7
F6
F6/9
it's spring.

THE SURREY WITH THE FRINGE ON TOP

from OKLAHOMA!

Lyrics by OSCAR HAMMERSTEIN II
Music by RICHARD RODGERS

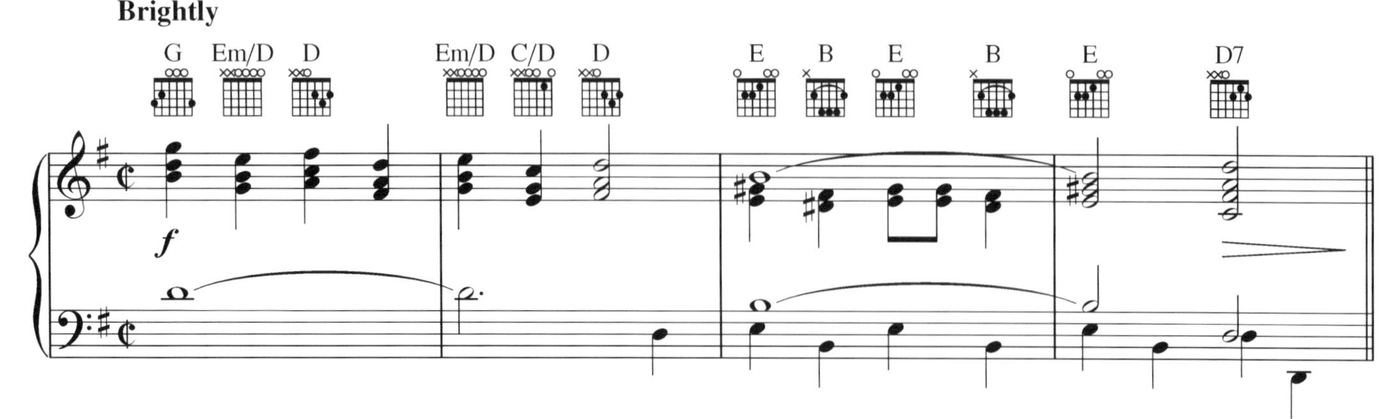

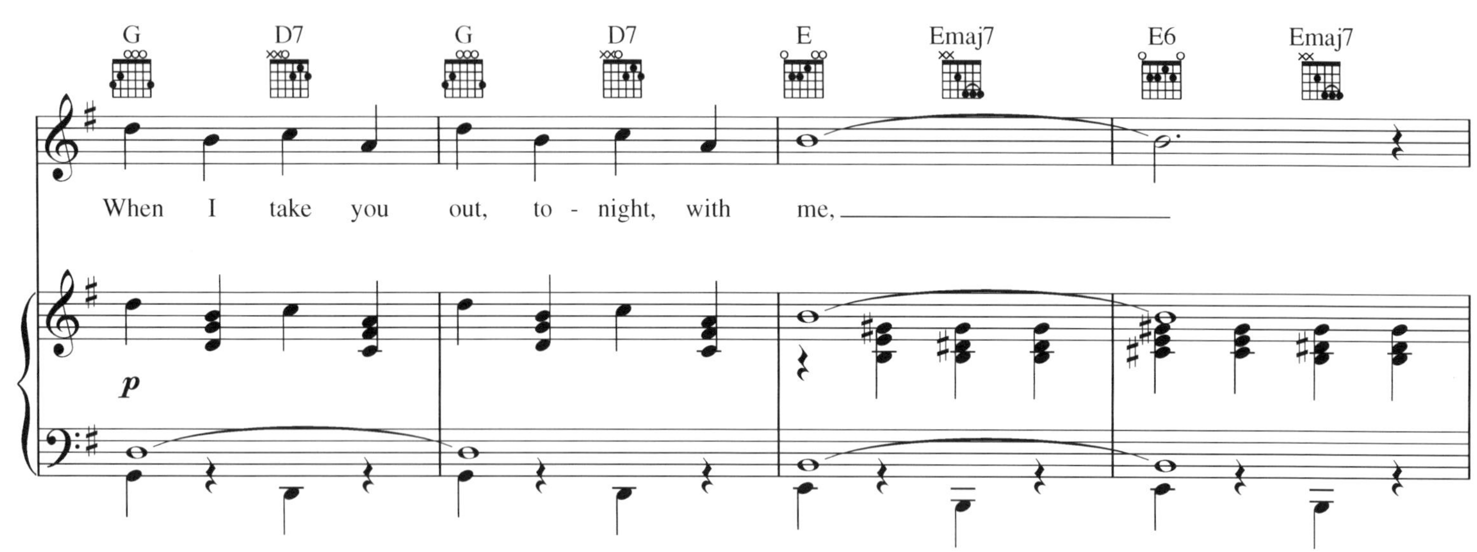

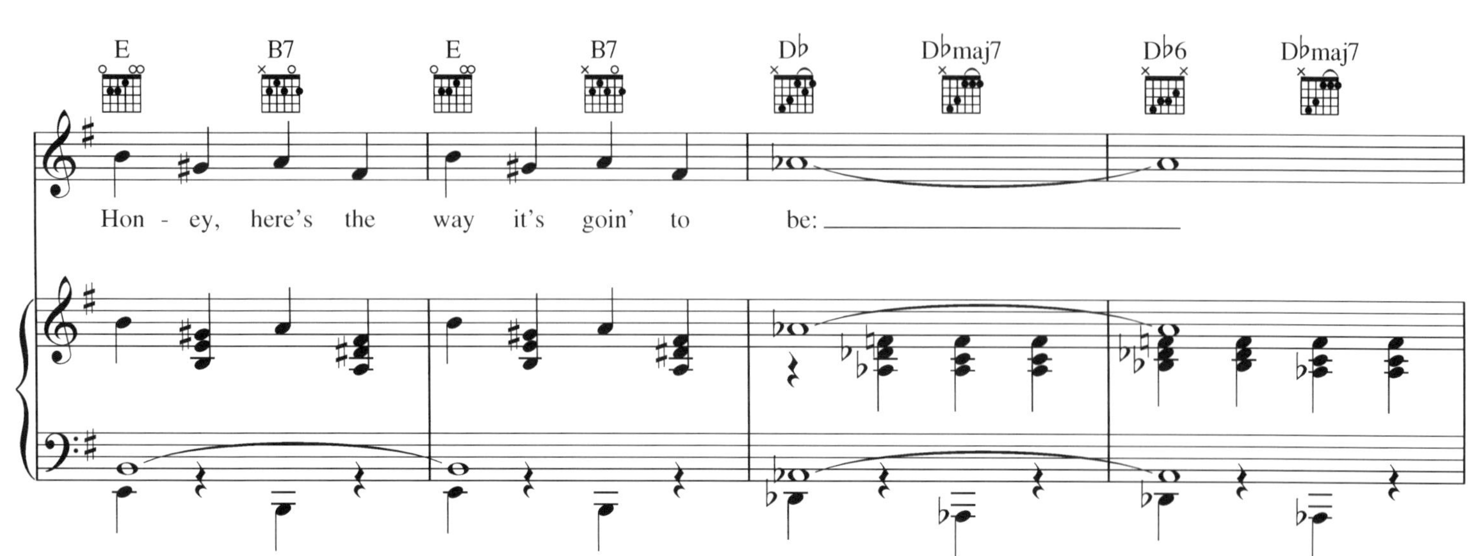

D♭
A♭7
D♭
A♭7
B♭/F
E♭/F
F7
You will set be - hind a team of snow - white hors - es,
G/D
D7
G/D
D7
G
in the slick - est gig you ev - er see!
mf
Refrain
G
Gmaj7
G6
G
Gmaj7
Chicks and ducks and geese bet - ter scur - ry when I take you
All the world - 'll fly in a flur - ry when I take you
I can see the stars get - tin' blur - ry when we drive back
p - mf
G6
Gmaj7
G
Gmaj7
G6
G
out in the sur - rey, when I take you out in the sur - rey with the
out in the sur - rey, when I take you out in the sur - rey with the
home in the sur - rey, driv - in' slow - ly home in the sur - rey with the

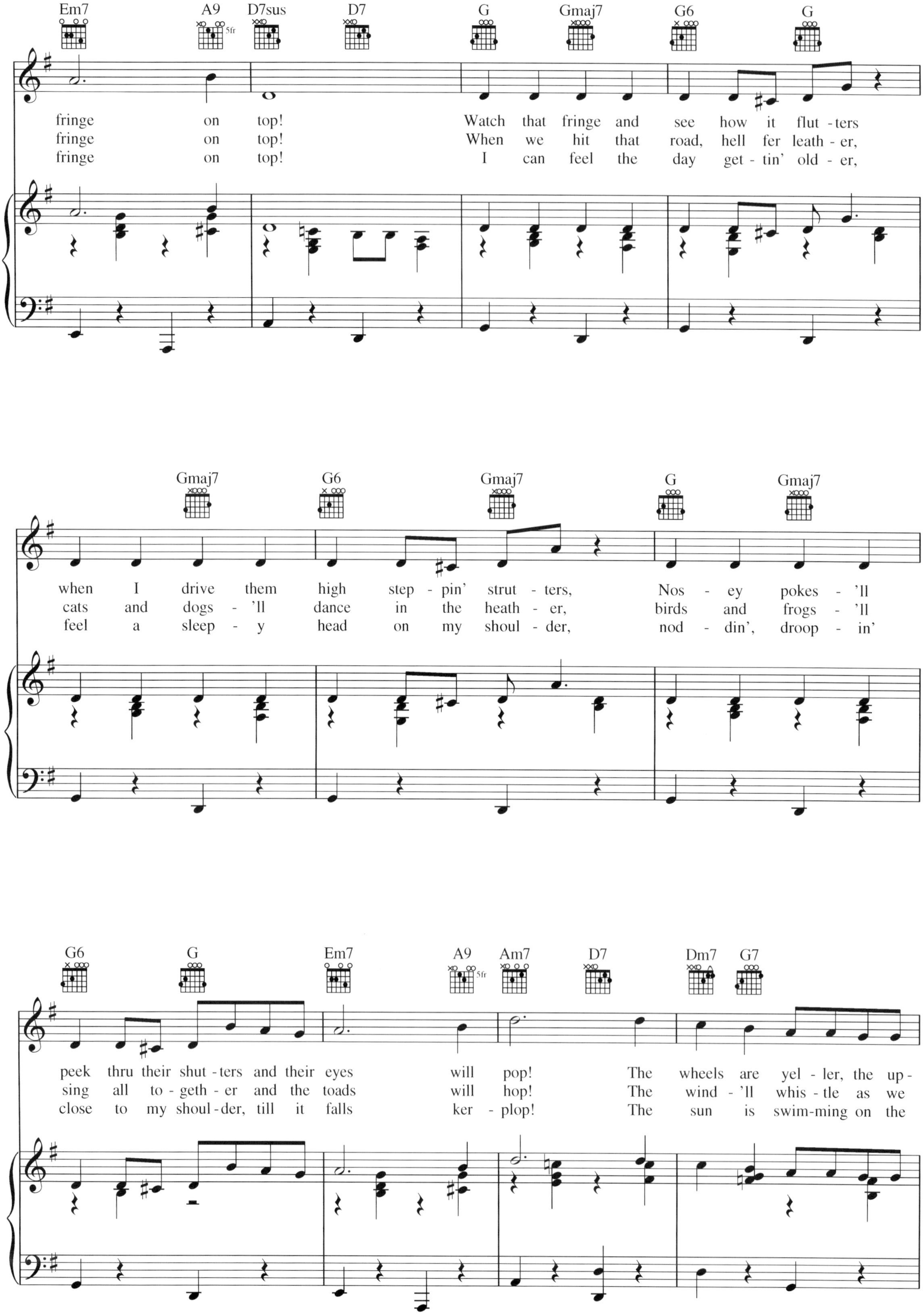

Em7 A9 D7sus D7 G Gmaj7 G6 G

fringe on top! Watch that fringe and see how it flut - ters
fringe on top! When we hit that road, hell fer leath - er,
fringe on top! I can feel the day get - tin' old - er,

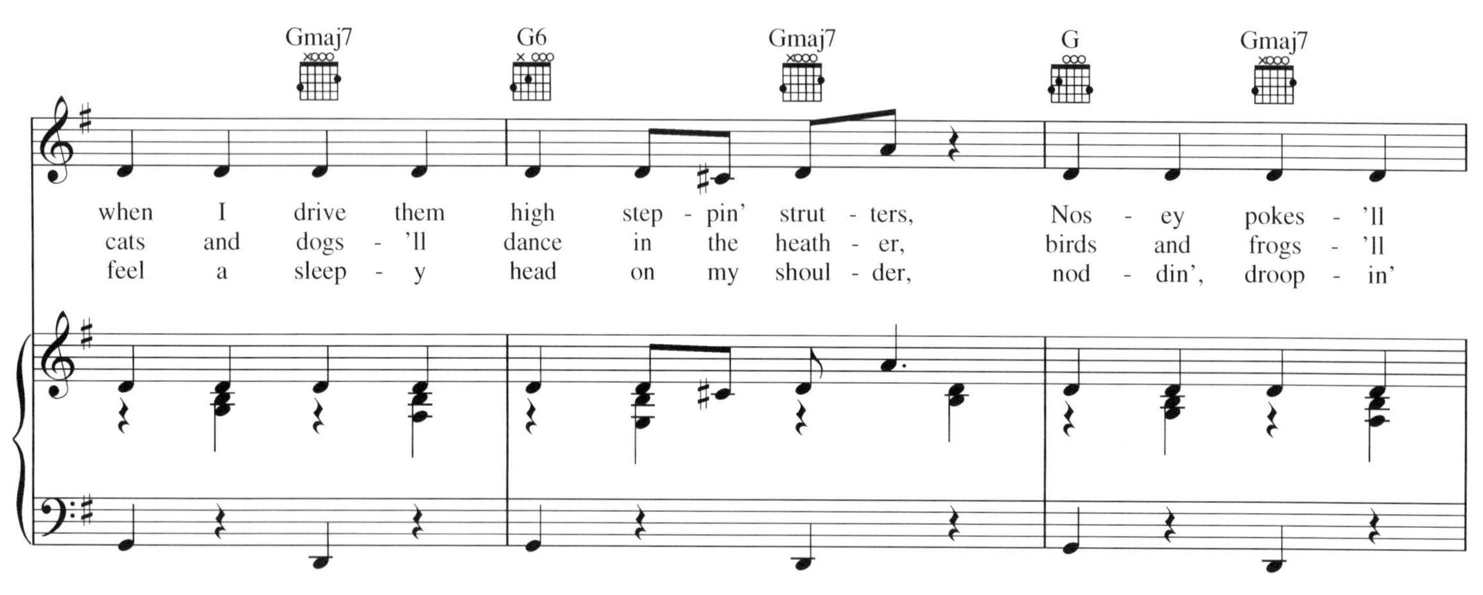

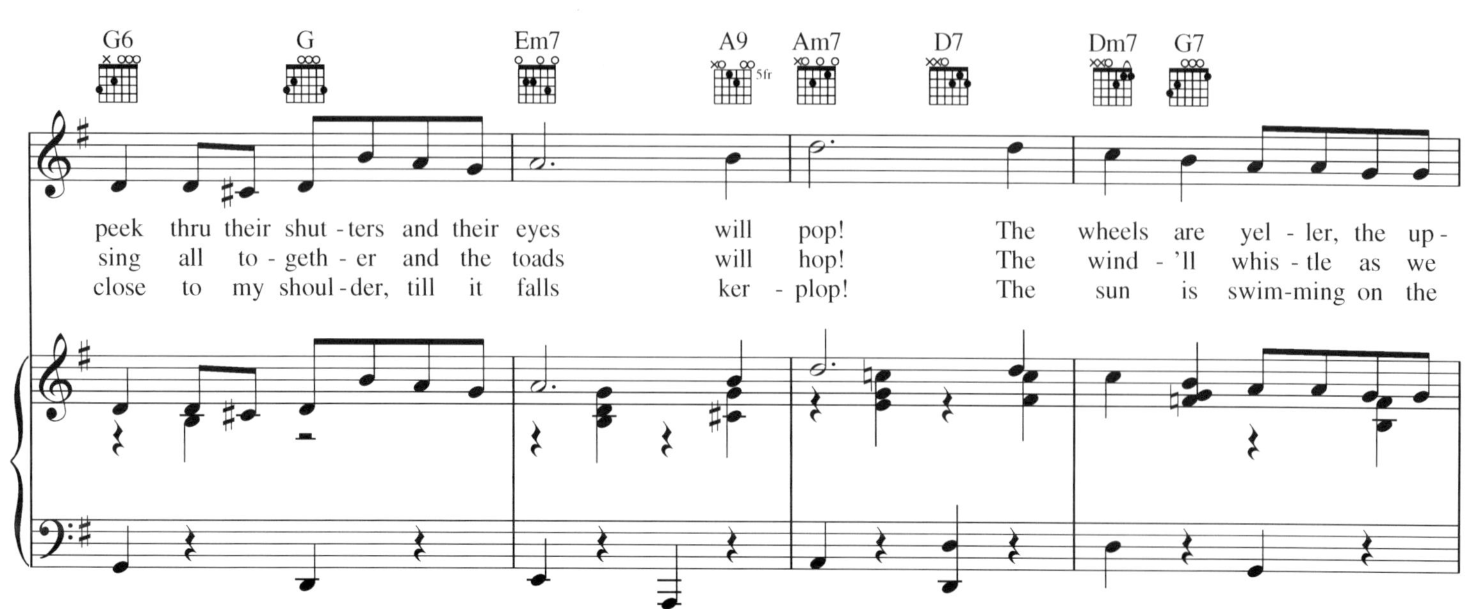

Cmaj7
G7sus
G7
C
hol - ster - y's brown, the dash - board's gen - u - ine leath - er, with
rat - tle a - long, the cows - 'll moo in the clo - ver, the
rim of a hill, the moon is tak - in' a head - er, and
Em7
A7
D
Em7
A7
is - in - glass cur - tains y' can roll right down, in case there's a change in the
riv - er will rip - ple out a whis - pered song, and whis - per it o - ver and
jist as I'm think - in' all the earth is still, a lark - 'll wake up in the
Am7/D
D7
G
Gmaj7
G6
G
Gmaj7
weath - er. Two bright side - light's wink - in' and blink - in', ain't no fin - er
o - ver: Don't you wisht y'd go on for - ev - er? Don't you wisht y'd
med - der. Hush, you bird, my ba - by's a - sleep - in'! May - be got a
p

G6
Gmaj7
G
Gmaj7
G6
G
rig, I'm a - think - in' you c'n keep your rig if you're think - in' 'at I'd
go on for - ev - er? Don't you wisht y'd go on for - ev - er and ud
dream worth a - keep - in', whoa! you team, and jist keep a - creep - in' at a

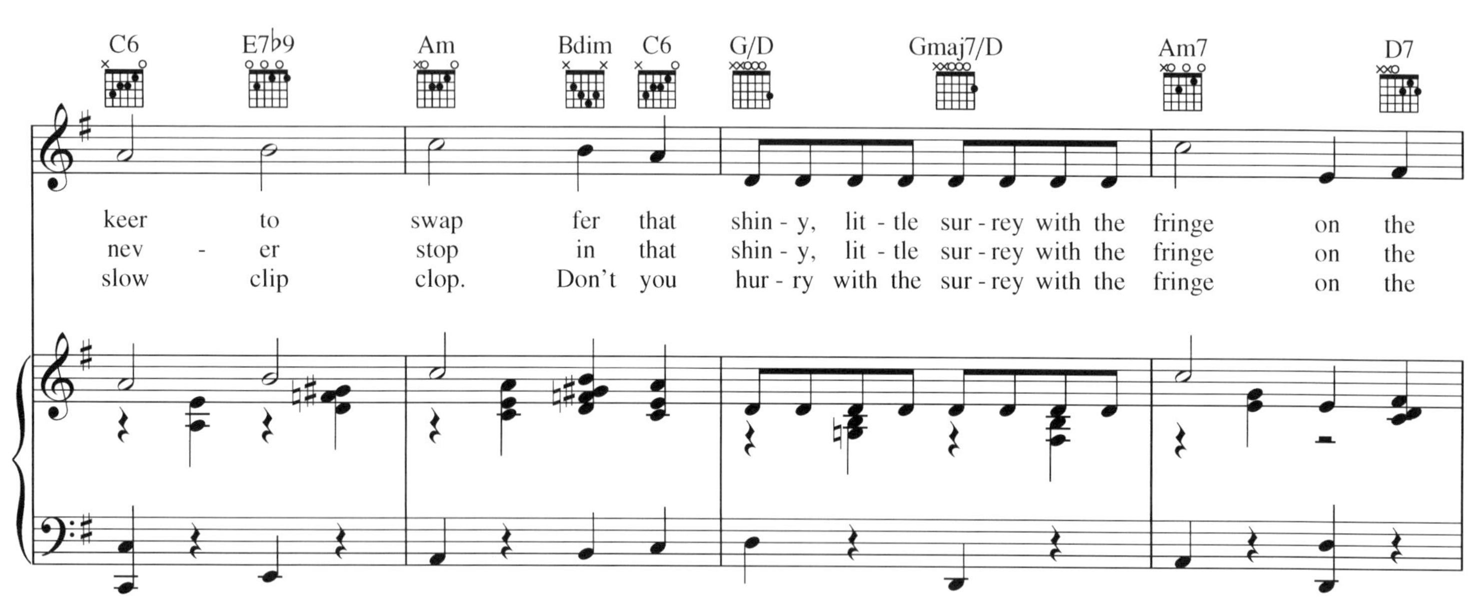
C6
E7♭9
Am
Bdim
C6
G/D
Gmaj7/D
Am7
D7
keer to swap fer that shin - y, lit - tle sur - rey with the fringe on the
nev - er stop in that shin - y, lit - tle sur - rey with the fringe on the
slow clip clop. Don't you hur - ry with the sur - rey with the fringe on the

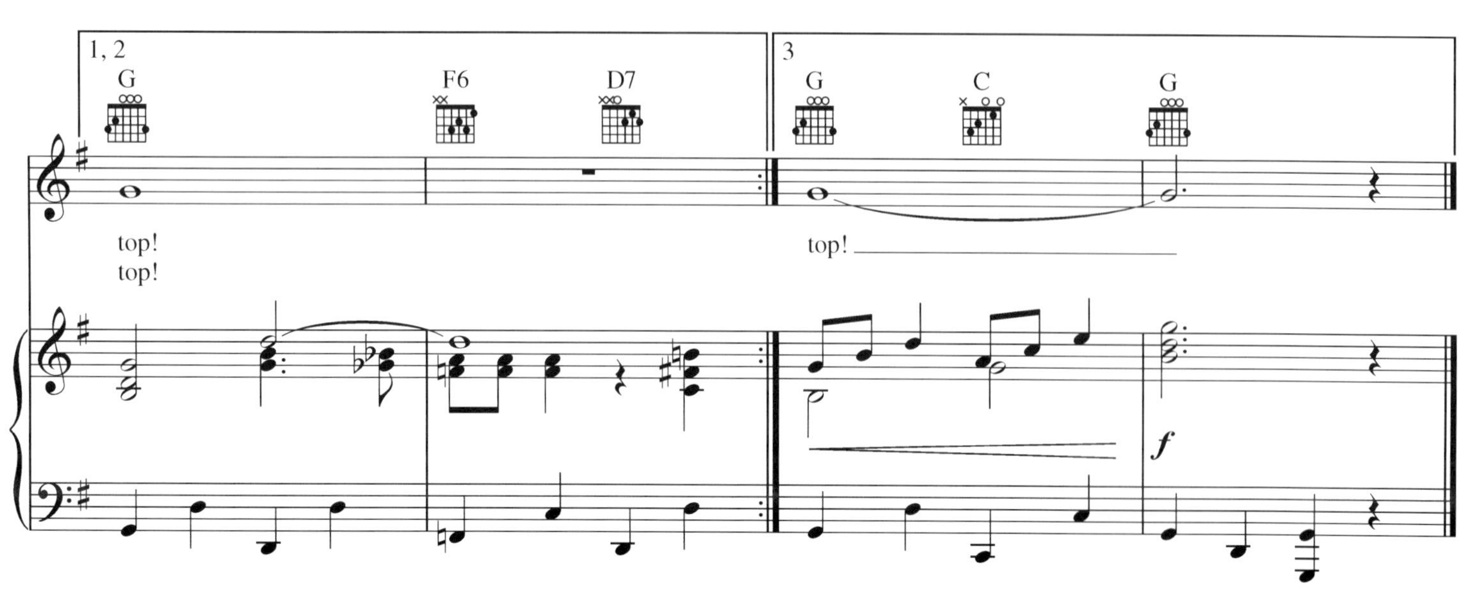
1, 2
G
F6
D7
3
G
C
G
top!
top!
top!
f

THAT OLD BLACK MAGIC

from the Paramount Picture STAR SPANGLED RHYTHM

Words by JOHNNY MERCER
Music by HAROLD ARLEN

Bb9#5/Eb
4fr
Eb6
Bb9#5
same old witch - craft when your eyes meet mine. The
Eb
3fr
same old tin - gle that I feel in - side, and
cresc. poco a poco
Db
Db7
4fr
then that el - e - va - tor starts its ride, and
rit.
f a tempo
Ab6
3fr
Abm6
4fr
Ebmaj9
C+
down and down I go, 'round and 'round I go
dim. poco a poco

Fm7
Emaj7
E♭
like a leaf that's caught in the tide. I should
p
mf
Cm
A♭9♯11
stay a - way but what can I do? I hear your
G9
C9
name and I'm a - flame, a -
Fm
D♭9
flame with such a burn - ing de - sire that on - ly your

A♭m6
4fr
B♭13
5fr
kiss can put out the fire. For
3
pp
p
E♭
3fr
you're the lov - er I have wait - ed for, the
B♭m7/E♭
6fr
E♭9
mate that fate had me cre - at - ed for, and
cresc. poco a poco
A♭
4fr
A♭m6
4fr
ev - 'ry time your lips meet mine, dar - ling,
f

A♭6/9
A♭m6
4fr
E♭maj7
3fr
C+
down and down I go, 'round and 'round I go
dim.
p
Fm7/E♭
Fm7♭5/E♭
6fr
3
in a spin, lov - ing the spin I'm in, un - der that
B♭7sus/E♭
6fr
1
E♭6
old black mag - ic called love! That
rit.
a tempo
2
E♭6
Fm7♭5/E♭
6fr
E♭6/9
5fr
love!
a tempo
rit. e dim.
pp

TANGERINE

from the Paramount Picture THE FLEET'S IN

Words by JOHNNY MERCER
Music by VICTOR SCHERTZINGER

A/E
Bm
E7
Em7/A
A7
D7♯5
treme, wait till you see her face. Tan - ger -
Gm7
C7
F6
ine, she is all they claim,
F6/A
A♭dim7
Gm7
C7
Gm7
C7
with her eyes of night and lips as bright as
Fmaj7
F6
D7♯5
Gm7
flame. Tan - ger - ine,

C7
F6
E7
when she danc - es by, se - ño -
A
F♯m7
Bm7
E9
A7
ri - tas stare and ca - ba - lle - ros sigh.
D7
D7♯5
Gm7
C7
F6
And I've seen toasts to Tan - ger - ine
F6/A
A♭dim7
Gm7
C7
Gm7
C7
C7/B♭
raised in ev - 'ry bar a - cross the Ar - gen -

A7
D7
Gm
Gm/F
3fr
3
tine.
Yes, she has them all on the
Em7
A7
Dm7
F/G
G7
run, but her heart be - longs to just one. Her
Bb
Gm7
Gm7/C
C7
1
F
Cm/Eb
heart be - longs to Tan - ger - ine.
D7
D7#5
2
F
F6/9
Tan - ger - ine.
rit.

THANKS FOR THE MEMORY

from the Paramount Picture BIG BROADCAST OF 1938

Words and Music by LEO ROBIN
and RALPH RAINGER

B♭6
B♭m6/D♭
C7
C13
love - ly it was! Thanks for the
love - ly it was! Thanks for the
F6
F♯dim7
mem - o - ry of rain - y af - ter - noons,
mem - o - ry of lin - ge - rie with lace,
C7/G
F/A
D♯dim7
C7/E
swing - y Har - lem tunes, and mo - tor trips and burn - ing lips and
Pils - ner by the case, and how I jumped the day you trumped my
F♯dim7
Gm7
Adim7
B♭6
burn - ing toast and prunes. How love - ly it
one and on - ly ace. How love - ly it

B♭m6/D♭
3fr
C7
E♭7
A♭
4fr
E♭9
was! Man - y's the time that we feast - ed and
was! We said good - bye with a high - ball; then
A♭
4fr
Adim7
C/G
Am
man - y's the time that we fast - ed. Oh, well, it was swell while it
I got as "high" as a stee - ple. But we were in - tel - li - gent
Dm
Fm6/C
6fr
G7
Gm7
3fr
Gm7♭5
5fr
C7
C+
D♭dim7
last - ed; we did have fun and no harm done. And
peo - ple; no tears, no fuss, hur - ray for us. So
a tempo
C13
2fr
F6
F♯dim7
thanks for the mem - o - ry of sun - burns at the shore,
thanks for the mem - o - ry and strict - ly en - tre - nous,

C7/G
F/A
D♯dim7
C7/E
nights in Sing - a - pore. You might have been a head - ache but you
dar - ling, how are you? And how are all the lit - tle dreams that
1
F♯dim7
Gm7
Adim7
B♭6
C7
F
C7♯5
C7
nev - er were a bore, so thank you so much.
2
F♯dim7
Gm7
G♯dim7
F/A
nev - er did come true? Awf - 'ly glad I met you, chee - ri -
D♭7/A♭
Gm7
C7
D♭
F6
o and too - dle - oo and thank you so much!

THERE'S A SMALL HOTEL

from ON YOUR TOES

Words by LORENZ HART
Music by RICHARD RODGERS

Am7
D7
Gmaj7
G6
plete for us to share to - geth - er.
Gmaj7
G6
C
Dm7
G7
Look - ing through the win - dow you can
mf
C
D♯dim
E7
Am
see a dis - tant stee - ple; Not a sign of
E7
F
Am
Cm7
3fr
D7
Gmaj7
G6
peo - ple, Who wants peo - ple? When the
p

Gmaj7 G6 G
stee - ple bell says, "Good - night, sleep well," we'll
Am7
thank the small ho - tel
1
D7 Gmaj7 G6 Am7 D7
to - geth - er.
2
D7 B♭ Cm7 3fr F7
tel. We'll creep in - to our lit - tle shell And we will
G Am7 D7 Gmaj7
thank the small ho - tel to - geth - er.
rit.
L.H.
mf
Ped.

THESE FOOLISH THINGS
(Remind Me Of You)

Words by HOLT MARVELL
Music by JACK STRACHEY

Fm7/B♭ B♭7 E♭6 Cm7 Fm7 B♭7
you. A tin - kling pia - no in the next a - part - ment,
you. The park at eve - ning when the bell has sound - ed,
you. The smile of Gar - bo and the scent of ro - ses,
R.H.
E♭6 Cm7 F9 B♭7 E♭9
Those stum - bling words that told you what my heart meant, A fair-ground's paint - ed swings
The "Ile de France" with all the gulls a - round it, The beau - ty that is Spring's
The wait - ers whis - tling as the last bar clos - es, The song that Cros - by sings,
R.H.
A♭ C7 F9 B♭7 E♭ D7
These fool - ish things re - mind me of you.
These fool - ish things re - mind me of you.
These fool - ish things re - mind me of you.
Gm6 Cm6/D D9 Gm
You came, you saw, you con - quer'd
How strange, how sweet, to find you
How strange, how sweet, to find you

C9
B♭/F
Gm7/F
F9sus
F9
me; When you did that to me, I
still; These things are dear to me, They
still; These things are dear to me, They
B♭7
B♭dim7
Fm7/B♭
B♭7
E♭6
Cm7
knew some - how this had to be. The winds of March that make my
seem to bring you near to me. The sigh of mid - night trains in
seem to bring you near to me. The scent of smould - 'ring leaves, the
R.H.
Fm7
B♭7
E♭6
Cm7
F9
B♭7
E♭9
heart a danc - er, A tel - e - phone that rings but who's to an - swer? Oh, how the ghost of you
emp - ty sta - tions, Silk stock - ings thrown a - side, dance in - vi - ta - tions, Oh, how the ghost of you
wail of steam - ers, Two lov - ers on the street who walk like dream - ers. Oh, how the ghost of you
R.H.
A♭maj7
C7
F9
B♭7
1,2
E♭6
B♭dim7
B♭13
B♭7♯5
3
E♭
clings! These fool - ish things re - mind me of you.
clings! These fool - ish things re - mind me of you.
clings! These fool - ish things re - mind me of you.

THIS CAN'T BE LOVE
from THE BOYS FROM SYRACUSE

Words by LORENZ HART
Music by RICHARD RODGERS

Smoothly
G/D
C♯dim7/D
Am/D
D7
G6
Poor half - wit!
This can't be
poco rit.
p a tempo
C7
C13
G
love be - cause I feel so well,
No sobs, no sor -
G6
Am7
D7
Am7
D7
G6
- rows, no sighs;
This can't be love, I get no
mf
p
C7
C13
G/D
A7♭9
Am9
D7
diz - zy spell.
My head is not in the

G C6 C7 G/B F♯m7 B7 Em
skies. My heart does not stand still, Just hear it beat!
B7♯9 E7♯5(♭9) A9 D7♭9 4fr D7
This is too sweet to be love.
G6 C7 C13 2fr G6/D 3fr C♯dim7/D Am7
This can't be love be-cause I feel so well, But still I love to look
D7 1 G Am7 D7 2 G C7/B♭ Am7 Am7/D G
in your eyes. eyes.
mf
p

UNFORGETTABLE

Words and Music by
IRVING GORDON

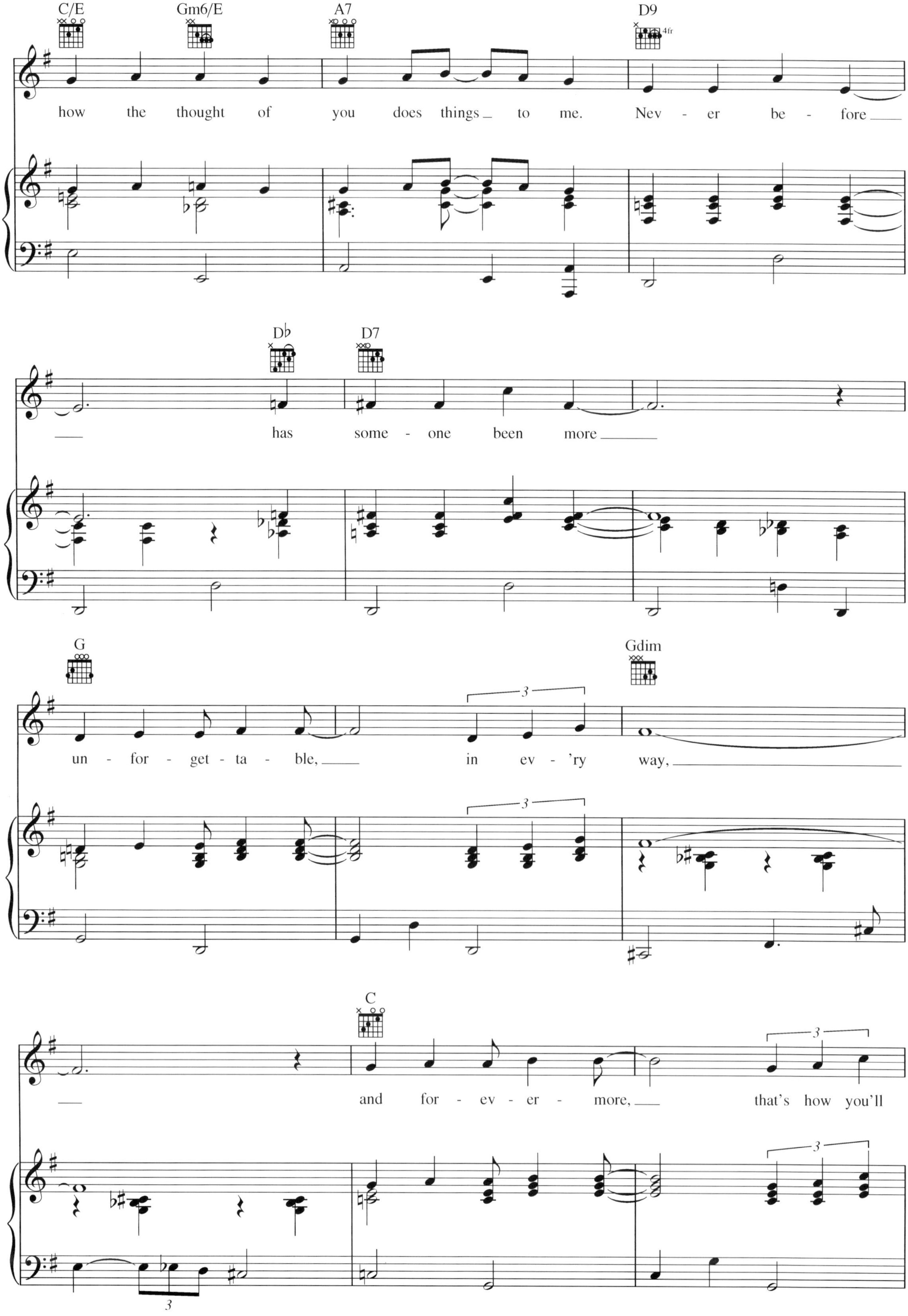

C/E Gm6/E A7 D9

how the thought of you does things to me. Nev - er be - fore

Db D7

has some - one been more

G Gdim

un - for - get - ta - ble, in ev - 'ry way,

C

and for - ev - er - more, that's how you'll

A9
Em7
Cm
A9
F
stay.
That's why, dar - ling,
Fm
C/E
Gm6/E
A7
it's in - cred - i - ble, that some - one so un - for - get - ta - ble
D7
G7
1
C
C♯7
thinks that I am un - for - get - ta - ble, too.
D13
C♯7
Am7/D
D7
2
C
Dm7
D♭7
C6
too.

THOU SWELL

from A CONNECTICUT YANKEE
from WORDS AND MUSIC

Words by LORENZ HART
Music by RICHARD RODGERS

Fm7 B♭9 E♭ D7 Fm7 B♭7♯5 E♭6 B♭dim7
3fr 6fr
Are you too wist - ful to care, Do say you care to
More thou wilt tell to San - dy. Thou art dan - dy; Now
Fm6 B♭7 E♭ Gm Cm D7 Gm
3fr 3fr 3fr 3fr
say; "Come near lad." You are so grace - ful, have you wings?
art thou my knight. Thine arms are mar - tial; Thou hast grace;
E♭ Cm D7 Gm Cm F7 B♭6 Gm
3fr 3fr 3fr 3fr 3fr
You have a face full of nice things; You have no speak - ing voice, dear,
My cheek is par - tial to thy face; And if thy lips grow wea - ry,
Cm E♭/F F7 A♭/B♭ B♭6 B♭7 F9 B♭7 F9 B♭7 F9
3fr 4fr
With ev - 'ry word it sings.
Mine are their rest - ing place.
Thou swell! Thou wit - ty! Thou

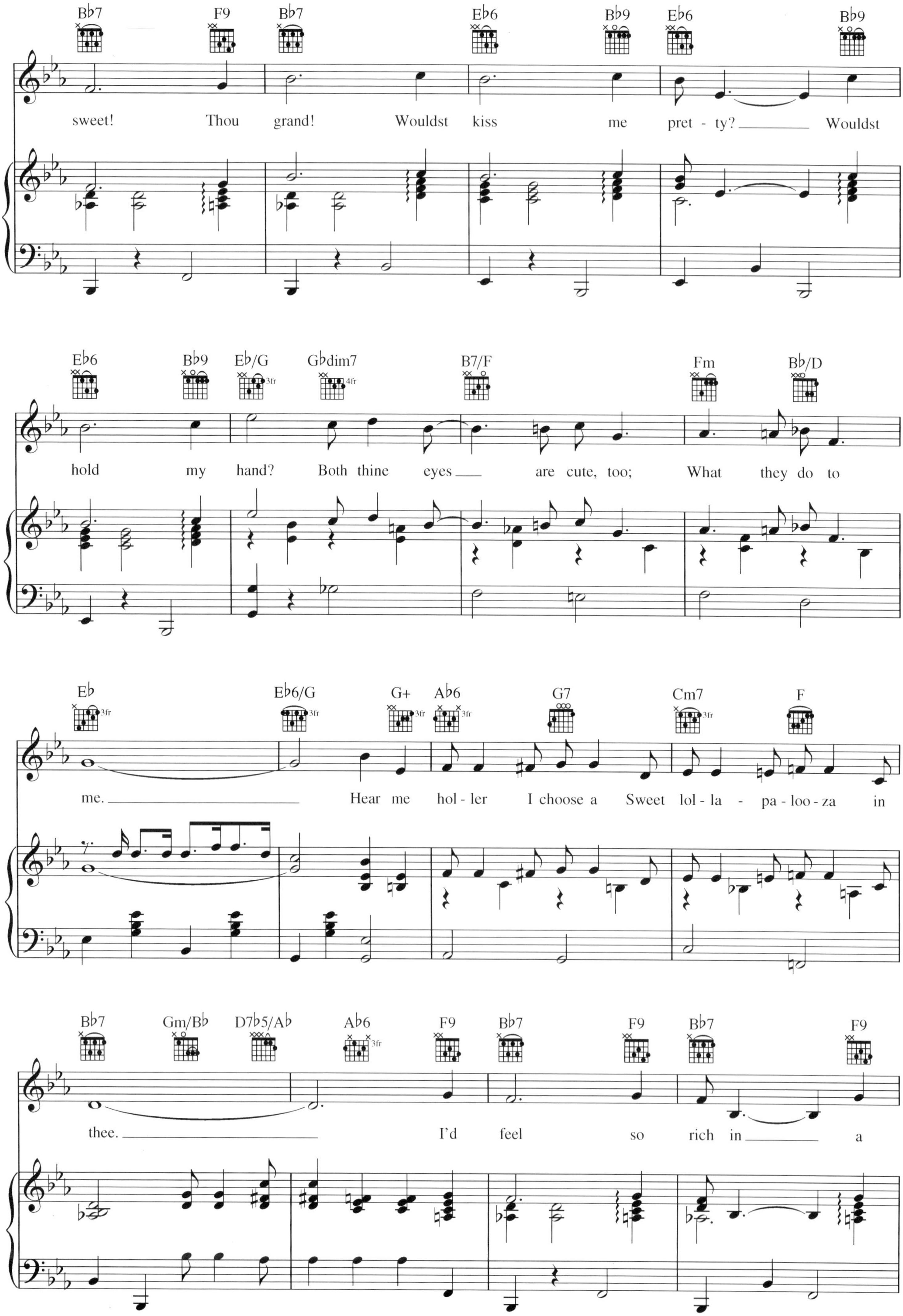
B♭7 F9 B♭7 E♭6 B♭9 E♭6 B♭9
sweet! Thou grand! Wouldst kiss me pret - ty? Wouldst
E♭6 B♭9 E♭/G G♭dim7 B7/F Fm B♭/D
3fr 4fr
hold my hand? Both thine eyes are cute, too; What they do to
E♭ E♭6/G G+ A♭6 G7 Cm7 F
3fr 3fr 3fr 3fr 3fr
me. Hear me hol - ler I choose a Sweet lol - la - pa - loo - za in
B♭7 Gm/B♭ D7♭5/A♭ A♭6 F9 B♭7 F9 B♭7 F9
3fr
thee. I'd feel so rich in a

B♭7
F9
B♭7
E♭6
B♭9
E♭6
B♭9
hut for two; Two rooms and kitch - en I'm
E♭6
B♭9
E♭/G
G♭dim7
B7/F
C/E
Fm
B♭/D
sure would do; Give me just a plot of, Not a lot of
G7
C+
C7
F7
F9
B♭7
land And Thou swell! Thou wit - ty! Thou
1
E♭
F♯dim7
B7/F
F9
2
E♭
Fm6/A♭
Cm7/G
B7/F
E♭
grand! Thou grand!

THE VERY THOUGHT OF YOU

Words and Music by
RAY NOBLE

A♭
B♭13
6fr
4fr
I don't need your por - trait, dear,
I'm sue - ing for dam - ag - es,
E♭7
Edim7
Fm
Fm7
Fm7♭5
to call you to mind,
For sleep - ing or
ex - cus - es won't do,
I'll on - ly be
A♭maj7/B♭
B♭13♭9
B♭m7
wak - ing, dear, I find;
sat - is - fied with you;
With a slow, easy swing
E♭9
N.C.
The ver - y thought of you, and I for -

A♭6
get to do the lit - tle
A♭ B♭m7 Bdim7 A♭/C B♭9
or - di - nar - y things that ev - 'ry - one ought to do.
D♭/F B♭m7 E♭7 Fm7 C7♯5
I'm liv - ing in a kind of day - dream, I'm
Fm Fm/E♭ Dm7♭5 G7♭9 Cm A♭m/C♭
hap - py as a king, and fool - ish tho' it

E♭/B♭
6fr
Bdim7
B♭m7
may seem, to me that's ev - 'ry -
E♭7
N.C.
A♭
4fr
thing. The mere i - dea of you, the long - ing
A♭6
3fr
here for you, You'll nev - er
A♭
4fr
B♭m7
Bdim7
A♭/C
3fr
B♭9
know how slow the mo - ments go 'til I'm near to you.

D♭/F
B♭m7
E♭7
Fm7
C7♯5
8fr
I see your face in ev - 'ry flow - er; your
Fm
Fm/E♭
Ddim7
N.C.
eyes in stars a - bove. It's just the
poco rit.
E♭7/B♭
6fr
Adim7
B♭m7
E♭13
5fr
1
A♭
4fr
Fm
thought of you, the ver - y thought of you, my love.
a tempo
B♭m7
E♭13
5fr
2
A♭
4fr
The ver - y love.
rit.

WATCH WHAT HAPPENS

from THE UMBRELLAS OF CHERBOURG

Music by MICHEL LEGRAND
Original French Text by JACQUES DEMY
English Lyrics by NORMAN GIMBEL

F9
Fm7
Bb9
Ebmaj7
Emaj7
and see in - to your heart,
Let him find you and watch what
Fmaj7
Gbmaj7
Gmaj7
G6
Gmaj7
G6
Gm7
C9
hap - pens. Cold.
No, I won't be - lieve your heart is cold,
Gm7
C9
F
F6
Fmaj7
F6
Fm7
Bb7
May - be just a - fraid to be bro - ken a - gain.
Fm7
Bb9
Bb7b9
Ebmaj7
Eb6
Ebmaj7
F9
Cm7
Let some - one with a deep love to give,

F9
Fm7
B♭9
Fm7
B♭9
Give that deep love to you and what mag - ic you'll
E♭
E♭6
E6
D6
E♭
E♭6
see: Let some - one give his heart, Some -
E6
D6
1
E♭maj7
E♭6
E♭maj7
E♭6
one who cares like me.
2
E♭maj7
E♭6
E♭maj7
E♭6
E♭
me.

WAVE

Words and Music by
ANTONIO CARLOS JOBIM

Bm7/E
E7
B♭9
A7
1
Dm7
G
- li - ness goes when - ev - er two can dream a dream to - geth - er.
Dm7
G
2
Dm7
G
Dm7
G
You can't de - er.
Gm7
C9/B♭
Am7
When I saw you first, the time was half past three.
A♭/B♭
4fr
B♭9/A♭
When your eyes met mine, it was e -

Gm7
A7♯5(♭9)
5fr
Dmaj9
4fr
ter - ni - ty. By now we know the
B♭dim7
Am7
D7♭9
4fr
wave is on its way to be. Just catch the wave;
Gmaj7
Gm6
3fr
F♯13
F♯7♯5
don't be a - fraid of lov - ing me.
B9
B7♭9
Bm7/E
E7
B♭9
A7
The fun - da - men - tal lone - li - ness goes when - ev - er two can dream a dream to - geth -

Portuguese Lyrics

Vou te contar, os olhos já não podem ver,
Coisas que só o coração pode entender.
Fundamental é mesmo o amor,
É impossível ser feliz sozinho.

O resto é mar, é tudo que não sei contar.
São coisas lindas, que eu tenho pra te dar.
Vem de mansinho abrisa e mediz,
É impossível ser feliz sozinho.

Da primeira vez era a cidade,
Da segunda o cais e a eternidade.

Agora eu já sei, da onda que se ergueu no mar,
E das estrelas que esquecemos de contar.
O amor se deixa surpreender,
Enquanto a noite vem nos envolver.

THE WAY YOU LOOK TONIGHT

Words by DOROTHY FIELDS
Music by JEROME KERN

2
E♭
E♭6
Fm
B♭7
G♭
Gm7♭5
A♭m
With each word your ten - der - ness grows, _
D♭7
G♭
B♭m
Adim7
D♭9
tear - ing my fear a - part,
G♭
G♭dim
A♭m7
D♭7
G♭maj7
E♭m
and that laugh that wrin - kles your nose touch - es my
B♭7sus
B♭7
E♭6
fool - ish heart.
Love - ly,

A♭
Fm7
B♭9
E♭9
C7
never, never change,
keep that breath - less charm,
Fm7
B♭7
E♭7
won't you please ar - range it, 'cause I love you,
rall.
A♭
Fm7
Gm
B♭7
E♭
E♭6
Fm9
B♭7
E♭maj7
E♭6
just the way you look to - night.
a tempo
A♭maj7
B♭7
A♭
G
Edim7
Fm
E♭6/B♭
B♭7
E♭6
Just the way you look to - night.
rall.

WHILE WE'RE YOUNG

Words by WILLIAM ENGVICK
Music by ALEC WILDER and MORTY PALITZ

A♭6
B♭7
E♭
E♭maj7
E♭6/G
Fm7(add4)
soft - ly.
Songs were made to sing
rall.
pp
mp
Fm7
Fm9/B♭
B♭13
B♭13♭9
while we're young.
accel.
rall.
E♭
E♭maj7
E♭6/G
Fm7
Ev - 'ry day is spring while we're
a tempo
Fm7/B♭
Dm7♭5/A♭
G7sus
G7
young.
accel.
rall.

Cm
Cm♯5
Cm
Cm6
Cm
None can re - fuse,
time
a tempo
Cm♯5
Cm
Cm7
Cm
Cm♯5
Cm/B♭
flies so fast,
too dear to
Adim(add4)
Adim
A♭6
Fm9
Fm7
lose and too sweet to
f
mp
rall.
Fm9/B♭
B♭13
E♭
E♭maj7
E♭6/G
Fm7(add4)
last. Though it may be just
a tempo

Fm7
Fm9/B♭
B♭13
6fr
B♭13♭9
6fr
for to - day
accel.
rall.
E♭
3fr
E♭maj7
3fr
E♭6/G
3fr
Fm7
share our love we must, while we
a tempo
Fm7/B♭
Dm7♭5/A♭
3fr
G7sus
G7
may.
accel.
rall.
Cm
3fr
Cm(add2)/B
7fr
B♭m7
E♭7
B♭m
E♭7♭9
5fr
So blue the skies,
f
dim. poco a poco

Ab
Abm6
all sweet sur - prise
rall.
mp
Eb/Bb
Ebmaj7/Bb
Eb6/G
Fm7
Ab/Bb
Bb7b9
shines be - fore our eyes while we're
a tempo
1
Eb
F7b5(b9)/Bb
F13/Bb
F7b9/Bb
Fm7(add4)/Bb
Bb7b5(b9)
Bb13b9
Bb7b9
young.
mf
mp
rall.
2
Eb
F7b5(b9)/Eb
F13/Eb
F7b9/Eb
Fm7(add4)/Eb
Fm7b9/Eb
Eb(add2)
Eb
young.
mf
rall.
p

WHEN SUNNY GETS BLUE

Lyric by JACK SEGAL
Music by MARVIN FISHER

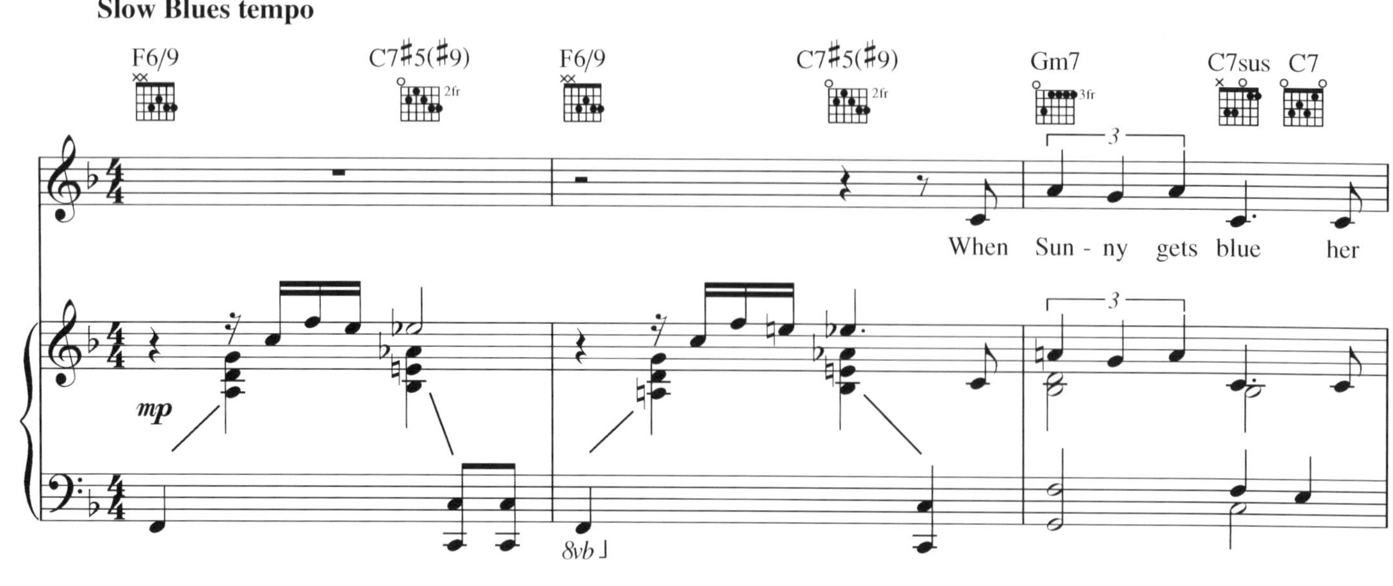

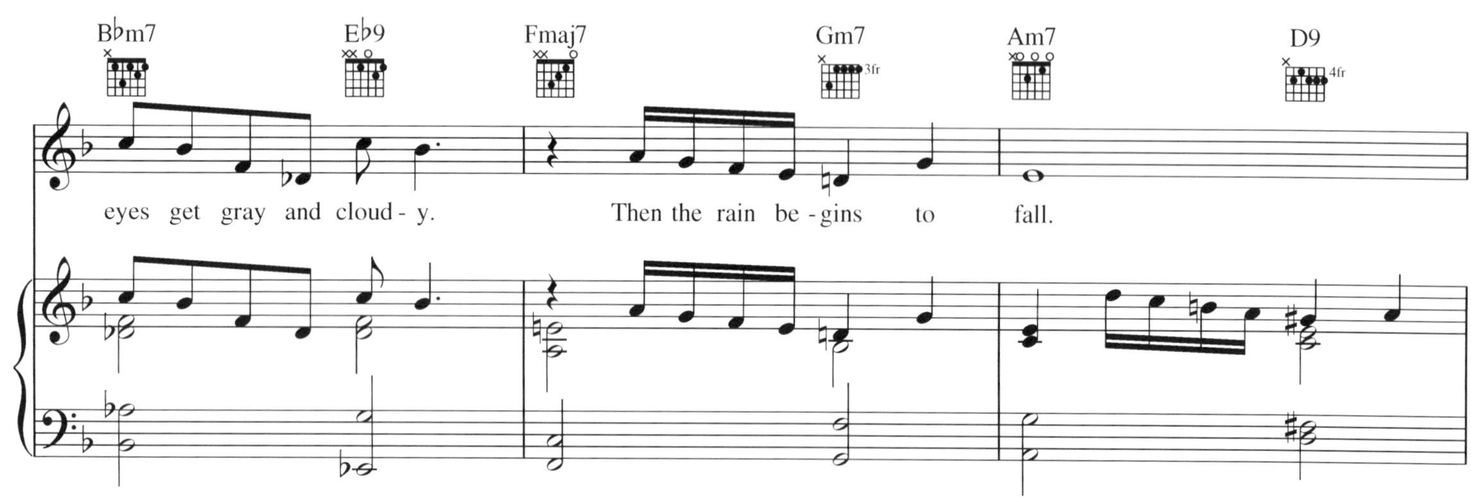

Gm7
C13
B♭13
A13
A7♭13
D9
D7♭9
Gm7
C7sus
C7
No sweet lov - er man comes to call. When Sun - ny gets blue, she
B♭m7
E♭9
Fmaj7
Gm7
breathes a sigh of sad - ness, like the wind that stirs the
Am7
D9
Bm7♭5
B♭m7
E♭9
trees. Wind that sets the leaves to sway - in',
Am7
A♭m7
D♭9
Gm7
C13
B♭13
like some vi - o - lins are play - in' weird and haunt - ing mel - o -

Em7
A7♭9
Dmaj7
Em7
dies.
Peo - ple used to love to
F♯m7
B9
B7♭9
Em7
A9
A7♭9
Dmaj7
hear her laugh, see her smile. That's how she got her name.
Dm7
G13
G7♭13
Cmaj7
Am7
Since that sad af - fair, she's lost her smile, changed her style.
F
Dm7
G7♭5
Gm7
C13♭9
C7♭13
Gm7
C7sus
C7
Some - how she's not the same.
But mem - 'ries will fade, and

Bbm7 Eb9 Fmaj7 Gm7 Am7 D9
pret - ty dreams will rise up where her oth - er dream fell through.
Bm7b5 Bbm7 Am7 Abm7 Db9
Hur - ry new love, hur - ry here to kiss a - way each lone - ly tear, and
Gm7 C7#5 F6/9 C7#5(#9) F6/9 C7#5(#9)
hold her near when Sun - ny gets blue.
8vb.
Gm7 C7#5 Gb9 F6/9 C7#5(#9) F6/9
Hold her near when Sun - ny gets blue.
rit.

WHERE OR WHEN

from BABES IN ARMS

Words by LORENZ HART
Music by RICHARD RODGERS

A♭ Fm7 Fm7♭5 Fm7/B♭ B♭7 E♭
4fr
3fr
Things you do come back to you, as though they knew the way. Oh, the
Fm B♭7 E♭ E♭6
3fr
tricks your mind can play! It seems we stood and talked like
poco rit.
a tempo
E♭maj7 Fm7
3fr
this be - fore. We looked at each oth - er in the same way then,
E♭maj7 E♭6 Fm7♭5 B♭7
3fr
but I can't re - mem - ber where or when.

E♭
E♭6
E♭maj7
The clothes you're wear - ing are the clothes you wore. The
Fm7
smile you are smil-ing you were smil - ing then, but I can't re-mem - ber where or
E♭maj7
E♭6
Dm7♭5
G7
Cm
Fm7
when. Some things that hap - pen for the
G7sus
G7
F/G
G7
Cm
Fm7
first time, seem to be hap - pen - ing a -

Cm7
F7
Fm7/B♭
B♭7
E♭
E♭6
gain.
And so it seems that we have
E♭maj7
G+
A♭6
B♭6
met be - fore, and laughed be - fore, and
A♭6
Gm
Fm
B♭7
loved be - fore, but who knows where or
1
E♭
Fm/E♭
E♭maj7
Fm/E♭
B♭7sus
B♭7
when!
2
E♭
A♭m7
E♭
when!
rit.

WHY DO I LOVE YOU?

from SHOW BOAT

Lyrics by OSCAR HAMMERSTEIN II
Music by JEROME KERN

Dm7♭5
C/G
G7
heav - en. (There's more than sev - en, my heart dis -
C
E♭7
A♭/E♭
cov - ers.) In this sweet, im - prob - a - ble and un -
E♭9
E♭7
E♭7/D♭
A♭/C
3fr
real world, find - ing you has giv - en me my i -
B♭m7
E♭7
A♭
4fr
A♭dim7
deal world. Why do I love you?

E♭7 A♭ A♭6

Why do you love me? Why should there be two

E♭7 A♭/C

hap - py as we? Can you see the why or

B♭m7 E♭7 A♭6

where - fore I should be the one you

B♭m7 E♭7 A♭ A♭dim7

care for? You're a luck - y boy;

E♭7
A♭
A♭6
I am luck - y too. All our dreams of joy
E♭7
A♭7
seem to come true. May - be that's be - cause you
D♭maj7
B♭m7♭5
A♭/E♭
B♭m7
E♭7
love me. May - be that's why I love
1
A♭
you!
2
A♭
you!
8vb

WIVES AND LOVERS
(Hey, Little Girl)
from the Paramount Picture WIVES AND LOVERS

Words by HAL DAVID
Music by BURT BACHARACH

Gm7/C
Don't think be - cause there's a ring on your
Don't send him off with your hair still in
fin - ger you need - n't try an - y -
curl - ers, you may not see him a -
more.
gain.
C9
Cm7
3fr
F7♭9
For wives should al - ways
Am7♭5
D7
E♭maj7
3fr
be lov - ers too. Run to his

D7sus
D7
arms the moment he comes home to you.
I'm
He's
D♭maj7
C7sus
warn - ing you.
al - ways here.
Fm7
Hey, lit - tle girl, bet - ter wear some - thing pret - ty,
B♭9
E♭6
Edim7
some - thing you'd wear to go to the cit - y; And

Fm7
dim all the lights, pour the wine, start the mu - sic,
B♭9
E♭6
time to get read - y for love.
Oh,
Fm7
B♭9
Fm7
B♭9
time to get read - y, time to get read - y,
Fm7
B♭9
E♭6
time to get read - y for love.
8vb

YESTERDAYS

from ROBERTA
from LOVELY TO LOOK AT

Words by OTTO HARBACH
Music by JEROME KERN

A7
D7#5
D7
G7
Old - en days gold - en
Sad am I, glad am
C7#5
8fr
C7
F7
F#dim
9fr
Gm7
Gm7/F
Eb9
Eb7/Bb
6fr
days, days of mad ro - mance and
I, for to - day I'm dream - ing
Dm7/A
A7b9
5fr
Dm7
love, then gay
of yes - ter - days.
Gm7
A7b9
5fr
Dm7
rit.

YOU ARE TOO BEAUTIFUL

from HALLELUJAH, I'M A BUM

Words by LORENZ HART
Music by RICHARD RODGERS

Cmaj9
C9
Fmaj7♯5
F6
Cmaj7/G
G9
C6/G
Am7
thought that you'd a - dore me, but it was not a mir - a - cle, it was
A♭7♭5
Fmaj7/G
G9
Dm7
G9
mere - ly a mi - rage be - fore me. You are too beau - ti - ful, my
rit.
a tempo
Em7
A7♯5(♭9)
Dm7
G7♯5(♭9)
Cmaj7
Em7
E♭7
5fr
dear, to be true, and I am a fool for beau - ty.
Dm7
Dm7♭5
G7♭9
C6
Cmaj7
Cdim7
Dm7
G13
3fr
Fooled by a feel - ing that be - cause I had found you, I could have bound you,
3

C/E A7♭9 Dm7 G9 Em7 A7♯5(♭9)
5fr
too. You are too beau - ti - ful for one man a - lone, for
Dm7 G7♯5(♭9) Cmaj7 Em7 E♭7 Dm7 Dm7♭5 G7♭9
one luck - y fool to be with, when there are oth - er men with
C6 G♯dim7 Am7 D7 Dm7/G G7♭9 C6 F F♯dim7
6fr
3
eyes of their own to see with. Love does not stand
C/G C♯dim7 Dm7 Dm7/G G13 Cmaj9 C6 Bm7♭5 E7
3fr
shar - ing, not if one cares. Have you been com -

Am
Am7
Am7/D
D9
Dm7/G
G7
paring my ev'ry kiss with theirs?
Dm7
G9
Em7
A7♯5(♭9)
Dm7
G7♯5(♭9)
If on the other hand, I'm faithful to you, it's not through a sense of
Cmaj7
Em7
E♭7
Dm7
Dm7♭5
G7♭9
C6
G♯dim7
Am7
duty. You are too beautiful and I am a fool for
D7
Dm7/G
G7♭9
C6
Fmaj7
Cmaj7/E
A♭9/E♭
C6
B♭6
C6/9
beauty. ty.

YOU BROUGHT A NEW KIND OF LOVE TO ME

from the Paramount Picture THE BIG POND

Words and Music by SAMMY FAIN,
IRVING KAHAL and PIERRE NORMAN

Eb Cm/Eb Eb+ Eb Cm/Eb Eb+ Eb Eb+
you. Would you turn a - way or
Am7b5/Eb Cm6 F7
could you real - ly learn to care If I'd ev - er
F7b9 Bb11 Bb7
dare to say, "I love you." If the
poco rit.
Ped.
Fm7 Bb7 Eb Eb7/G F#dim
(not fast, with expression)
night - in - gales could sing like you They'd sing much sweet - er
p - mf a tempo

Fdim C7/E C7 F7 Bb11 Bb7 Eb6
than they do For you've brought a new kind of love to me.
mf
Bb11 Bb7 Fm7 Bb7 Eb Eb7/G F#dim
If the sand-man brought me dreams of you I'd want to sleep my
Fdim C7/E C7 F7 Bb11 Bb7 Eb Abm
whole life thru, For you've brought a new kind of love to me.
Eb Cm G/B Eb7/Bb Am7b5 Ab7 G7
I know that I'm the slave, you're the queen, But still you can un - der -
mf

Cm Bb/D F+ Bb6 Bdim7 F7/C F9
stand That un-der-neath it all you're a maid And I am on - ly a
Bb7 Ab/Eb Bb7/D F7 Bb7 Eb Eb7/G F#dim
man. I would work and slave the whole day thru, If I could hur - ry
p
Fdim C7/E C7 F7 Bb11 Bb7
home to you, For you've brought a new kind of love to
3
poco rit.
1
2
Eb Edim7 Ab/Bb Bbdim7 Bb7 Eb F7b5 Eb
me. If the me.
a tempo
mf

YOU DON'T KNOW WHAT LOVE IS

Words and Music by DON RAYE
and GENE DePAUL

Fm6
Db9
lose, you don't know what
Gm7/C
C7
Fm6
love is. You don't know how
Db9
C7#5
8fr
Fm6
Gb9
3fr
3
lips hurt un - til you've kissed and had to pay the
3
Db9
Bb9
Gb9
3fr
cost; un - til you've flipped your heart and you have

Fm6
D♭9
G♭9
3fr
Fm6
lost, you don't know what love is. Do
B♭m7
A7
A♭maj7
A♭6
3fr
B♭m7
E♭7
A♭maj7
you know how a lost heart fears the thought of rem - in - isc -
Dm7
G9
9fr
Cmaj7
C7
- ing? And how lips that taste of tears
D♭9
C9
Fm6
lose their taste for kiss - ing? You don't know how

D♭9
C7♯5
8fr
Fm6
G♭9
3fr
3
hearts burn ___ for love that can - not live, yet ___ nev - er
3
D♭9
B♭9
G♭9
3fr
dies, un - til you've faced each dawn with sleep - less
Fm6
D♭9
G♭7
eyes, you don't know ___ what
1
Fm6
love is. ___ You
2
Fm6
F6
love is. ___

YOU'VE CHANGED

Words and Music by BILL CAREY
and CARL FISCHER

Slowly, with feeling
Bb Gm Cm7 F7b9 Bb7 Fm7 Bb7 Bb7#5 Ebmaj7 Eb
hon - est - ly be - lieve that you are bored. You've changed, that
mp - mf
D7 D7#5 D7 Bbm6 C7 C7#5
spar - kle in your eyes is gone, your smile is just a care - less
F13 F9#5 F9 B9 Bb6/9 B7#5 Eb Cm
yawn, you're break - ing my heart, you've changed.
Fm7 Bb7 B7#5 Ebmaj7 Eb D7 D7#5 D7
You've changed, your kiss - es now are so bla -

B♭m6
C7
C7♯5
F13
F9♯5
F9
sé, you're bored with me in ev - 'ry way, I
B9
B♭9
E♭7
Cm
D♭
E♭7
E♭+
can't un - der - stand, you've changed. You've for -
A♭maj7
A♭m7
Gm7
got - ten the words, "I love you," each mem - o - ry that we've shared.
E♭
B♭7♯5
E♭7
E♭+
A♭maj7
A♭m7
A♭m(maj7)
You ig - nore ev - 'ry star a - bove you, I can't

E♭ Gbm6 B♭7 Fm7 B♭7♯5 B♭7+ E♭maj7 E♭
re - a - lize you ev - er cared. You've changed, you're
D7 D7♯5 D7 B♭m6 C7 C7♯5
not the an - gel I once knew, no need to tell me that we're
F13 F9♯5 F9 B9 B6/9 Ddim7
through, it's all o - ver now, you've changed.
1
E♭6 B9
f
E9♭5 B♭7 B♭7♯5
You've
mf
2
E♭6 A♭m7 E♭maj7 E♭6
poco rit.
pp

WITCHCRAFT

Lyric by CAROLYN LEIGH
Music by CY COLEMAN

D7♭9sus
D7
Gm
G♭maj7
make ad-vanc - es, oh no!
Un - der nor - mal
Gm7/C
C7♭9
Am
Dm7
Gm7
C7♭9
cir - cum - stanc - es, I'd go but oh!
F
G♯dim7
Those fin - gers in my hair,
that sly, come -
Gm7
Gm7/C
C7
hith - er stare
that strips my con-science bare,
it's

Fmaj7
F6
B♭maj7
witch - craft.
And I've got
B♭m
no de - fense for it, the heat is too in - tense for it,
Fm/A♭
G7♯5
Cmaj9
what good would com - mon sense for it do?
C7
Fmaj9
F
'Cause it's witch - craft!
Wick - ed

C11/F
6fr
C7
Fmaj9
witch - craft.
And al - though I know
F6
Bm7♭5
E7
Am
it's strict - ly ta - boo.
When you a -
Am♯5
5fr
Am6
Am♯5
5fr
Am
rouse the need in me,
my heart says,
"Yes, in - deed" in me.
Gm
3fr
Gm♯5
3fr
Gm7
"Pro - ceed with what you're lead - in' me to!"

C7
F6
It's such an an - cient pitch
G♯dim7
but one I would - n't switch
Gm7
'cause there's no
Gm7/C
E6/C
1
F6
nic - er witch than you!
2
N.C.
E♭7
you!
N.C.
E♭7
N.C.